10 $\frac{00}{}$

PSYCHOPHYSIOLOGY OF LEARNING AND MEMORY

PSYCHOPHYSIOLOGY OF LEARNING AND MEMORY

By

ELIO MAGGIO, M.D., F.I.C.A., M.A.A.A.S.

Instructor of Psychiatry
Columbia University College of Physicians and Surgeons
Clinical Instructor of Psychiatry
The Mount Sinai School of Medicine
Staff Member Department of Psychiatry
Harlem Hospital Center
Clinical Assistant Psychiatrist
The Mount Sinai Hospital
New York, New York
"Privat Dozent" of Biochemistry and Otolaryngology
University of Naples College of Medicine
Naples, Italy

With a Foreword by

Vito Maria Buscaino, M.D.

Professor Emeritus of Neurology and Psychiatry
University of Naples College of Medicine
Naples, Italy

CHARLES C THOMAS • PUBLISHER

Springfield • *Illinois* • *U.S.A.*

Published and Distributed Throughout the World by

CHARLES C THOMAS • PUBLISHER

BANNERSTONE HOUSE

301-327 East Lawrence Avenue, Springfield, Illinois, U.S.A.

NATCHEZ PLANTATION HOUSE

735 North Atlantic Boulevard, Fort Lauderdale, Florida, U.S.A.

With THOMAS BOOKS *careful attention is given to all details of
manufacturing and design. It is the Publisher's desire to present books
that are satisfactory as to their physical qualities and artistic possibilities
and appropriate for their particular use.* THOMAS BOOKS *will be true
to those laws of quality that assure a good name and good will.*

Printed in the United States of America

JJ-1

To my wife, Wanda,

whose psychological growth—more than any specific learning experience and memory ability—is leading her toward the Ph.D. in psychology.

To my parents,

who emotionally and behaviorally have contributed significantly to the accomplishment of this endeavor.

To all good learners and forgetters,

who make life appear more interesting and worthwhile.

Without memory the past would vanish, intelligence would be absent and life would be indeed "a tale told by an idiot, full of sound and fury, signifying nothing."

RALPH W. GERARD

The brain secretes thoughts as the liver secretes bile.

THOMAS H. HUXLEY

Physiologically different brains are made, not born.

ROBERT B. LIVINGSTON

FOREWORD

Psychophysiology of Learning and Memory, written by a distinguished and internationally-known scholar and scientist, Dr. Elio Maggio, is a fundamental study that is impressive not only because of the accurate and extensive richness of the data but also because of the essentially genetic and biological interpretation given to them.

This book thoroughly covers the field of human learning and memory. First, it discusses in detail the most relevant psychological and physiological material resulting from a capillary analysis of the literature. Second, it contains an important interpretive section, placing strong emphasis on the concept of "psychic activity" being the result of "biological activity," i.e. the neurological activity in the nerve cells and fibers, and the neuronal response to chemical events capable of activating nerve tissue.

Although not cited in this book, the data showing the existence of a "chemical language" in the nonhuman world, especially insects, are quite numerous and supplement Dr. Maggio's data on human learning and memory and support his biological interpretation.

Dr. Maggio has the courage to express what most seem to ignore and only a few consider possible, i.e. that the human "psyche" is the result of brain biological functioning rather than the activity of specific extraneurological entities.

One admires the intelligence, ability, and wide range of knowledge of a scholar like Dr. Maggio, and is stimulated to a careful reading of this most instructive book.

Vito Maria Buscaino, M.D.

PREFACE

The idea of writing about learning and memory had its roots in a lecture given at the New Jersey State Hospital, Greystone Park, N. J. in the fall of 1968. That was my first official presentation before a professional audience interested in psychiatry, psychology, and behavioral sciences after having been involved for two decades in different fields, from research and teaching basic sciences and otolaryngology in Europe and the United States, to medical practice in Italy.

It seemed imperative for me as a prospective psychiatrist to deepen also the knowledge of the learning and memory processes because they represent the most essential attribute of total brain functioning. The subject is as fascinating as it is difficult, complex, and multifaceted. My reaction to its treatment in the current literature has been one of disappointment because of the inadequate integration of the several types of information available on the subject matter. It has "sublimated," however, as stronger motivation in developing, in a written form, my own critical evaluation of the psychophysiological aspects of learning and memory.

As the title of this monograph suggests, learning and memory are not approached from the clinical standpoint, i.e. as an expression of a disordered function; the diagnostic and therapeutic aspects of the amnesic and paramnesic syndromes are discussed just *en passant*. This is because the study of learning and memory alterations does not contribute significantly to the understanding of the mechanisms of normal function. Learning tests, such as those intended to determine type, amount, and complexity of the information mastered by the individual, are also more important in the study of normal than of abnormal function. As a matter of fact, most patients affected by memory disorders do not benefit enough from repeated exposure to learning material, nor from the allotment of additional time to achieve a given criterion of learning. The clinical assessment of a memory impairment is not factually supported by the use of any test also because performance in both learning and memory depends upon several processes which could be impaired independently from the others and to a different degree from each other. Even the techniques based on the individual testing of the processes responsible for learning and memory are somewhat unreliable because of the final composite score additively derived from its subtests.

Finally, when learning and memory are severely and irreversibly impaired, there is little that can be done therapeutically. Despite several advertised mnemotechnics it has been scientifically proven that past the phase of learning no available method improves retention or recall of experiential information. Therefore, it seems more interesting and valuable to focus the attention on the mechanisms of learning and memory in the attempt to unfold first theoretically and then experimentally and clinically new aspects of the cause-effect relationships between numerous events responsible for the phases and processes of those functions, and eventually perhaps to be able to control and correct the inherent disorders.

There is another reason, partly emotional in nature, for drawing my attention on learning and memory; it is my reaction to the training of two puppy dogs which recently joined my family. They have created a significant alternative with respect to psychiatric and neurologic patients as far as the understanding of the basic processes underlying learning and memory is concerned. Clinical observation, anyway, is unique in allowing for conceptualization of brain functioning and psychic phenomena. *How* learning occurs and *how* a perception becomes a permanent and retrievable memory trace, however, may be understood in depth only through a multidimensional and sophisticated experimentation in laboratory animals, research in man being limited to the study of the electrical events responsible in part for that functioning or to the study of learning and memory strictly as psychological processes. This experimental research should take in account all the possible factors which may interfere in the correct extrapolation of concepts from the data obtained in laboratory animals and those obtained in human beings. It has been shown recently, for example, that memory function is influenced by biological time of day. Day rhythm of memory has been discovered with peak of performance matching the peak of body temperature and motor activity during twenty-four hours. Even though such peak of biological activity in rodents occurs at night and in darkness, memory function in these animals has been usually tested during daytime when those nocturnal animals are supposed to sleep or at least to rest. On the other hand, most of the laboratory animals used to study learning and memory, such as rodents *in primis,* are very sensitive to environmental factors, thus providing interesting data which may have significant bearing on learning and memory functions of human beings, especially in relationship to the problem of education.

The validity of the concept that the survival and the future of mankind reside upon a complex cooperative behavior and that this, in turn, requires a technique of teaching and a method of education scientifically based in accordance with the biological and psychological aspects of learning and memory and general brain functioning as well, is just beginning to be recognized. The basic operations of educational institutions at all levels, however, are still outdated. A fundamental contribution to the understanding of how human beings learn and memorize in the different phases of their intellectual development has been given by the Swiss psychologist Jean Piaget and his co-workers over the past four decades, but it is only in the last few years that this knowledge has been accepted as scientifically valid even though not scientifically proven. On the other hand, the impressive body of scientific and clinical research of the last two decades has created a strong biological alternative to the psychological approaches and interpretations of learning and memory processes because of the integrated effort of many continental and American laboratories of neurophysiology, neurochemistry, and physiological psychology.

By presenting *Psychophysiology of Learning and Memory* to an audience of medical and nonmedical scholars, from the pure investigators to the teachers and students of mental functions and their behavioral expressions, I hope to have made a valuable contribution toward a better understanding of learning and memory and general brain functioning as well and to have also drawn attention to the social implications of the most significant research in this field. My study may also contribute in a long run to gaining a more intimate satisfaction from the analysis of psychological phenomena, even outside the domain of psychiatry, and involving more deeply the inner world of human beings. Perhaps it may also "catalyze" new trends of education, aiming primarily to apply new techniques and methods of teaching capable to produce creative and critical individuals in an environment in which the computer, the collective opinions, the slogans, and the preconceived trends of thoughts not only will help in shaping a better social life, but also preserve, and perhaps enhance, creativity and geniality.

ELIO MAGGIO

CONTENTS

PSYCHOPHYSIOLOGY OF LEARNING AND MEMORY

Chapter I

LEARNING AND MEMORY AS PSYCHOLOGICAL PROCESSES

GENERALITIES ABOUT LEARNING AND MEMORY

Psychological studies of learning and memory date back to many decades ago. They have been concerned primarily with the processes making those functions possible rather than with the biological mechanisms responsible for those functions. These mechanisms were ignored until about twenty years ago when the first neurophysiological approach to the study of learning and memory was made by the Canadian School of Psychology at the McGill University, Montreal. A few years later, it evolved into a biochemical or macromolecular approach, thanks to the Swedish School of Neurophysiology at the University of Göteborg. The effort of hundreds of investigators, among whom North Americans stand authoritatively, has been instrumental for making facts at least as numerous, valuable, and stimulating as speculations, hypotheses, and theories, not only as far as learning and memory are concerned, but also as general brain mechanics are concerned.

One of the difficulties of the scientific approach to the study of learning and memory is that the results of animal experimentation cannot be fully duplicated in men. No doubt, anyway, that a simple mechanistic approach is inadequate to the study of learning and memory processes and brain functioning in general. Memory is a past which is continuously integrated into the present when reexperienced, thus requiring a variety of psychophysiological mechanisms. Locating experience in time and place, relating it to other events, and giving it an actual significance appropriate to that experience which has passed in different periods of life results in making experiences real, living, meaningful events.

The development of the neurosciences over the past decade has contributed by throwing more light onto the basic mechanisms of brain functioning. Even the fundamental problem of the duality of brain and mind, which has interested a large number of scholars since ancient times, may be looked at in a different perspective. There is no specific evidence that mind is independent of brain functioning and that it is immaterial. There is, however, a great deal of experimental evidence that psychic phenomena are one of the expressions of brain functioning, as all the neurological ones. Certainly, by studying behavior, one can easily investigate one of the products of brain functioning, but behavior as a product is not necessarily the same as mind as a product, and it should not be confused with the mechanism underlying it. The immaterial nature of mind—or soul, as it has been also called by philosophers, theologists, and even by contemporary neurologists—can still be acceptable if one considers that a material mechanism should exist to account for its existence.

In ancient philosophy, when science was far from being so complex and sophisticated, and words were found for everything, material and immaterial, every abstraction deprived of material identity was interpreted as a spiritual entity, a reality behind the information provided by senses, an idea, a universal concept in contrast to the material entity closely related to the concrete data supplied by the sensory organs. In more modern times, however, the concept of matter has changed so radically, due to the progress of the physical sciences, that matter has become interchangeable with energy and information, quite contrasting to the static entity which underlies the dualistic concept of the universe.

An important part in the process or totality of mental functions, which is called *mind,* is represented by the functions of knowing and learning. (By so defining mind, the bias of considering it as something which *does,* rather than as a result of the brain's total mental operations, is overcome.) *Knowledge* results in "mapping" experiential information in the brain tissue and correlating and integrating it with other relevant information previously acquired and permanently stored as a memory. (The term "mapping" is used to signify the conversion of the sensory signals into the coding system. See below.) *Memory* is the mental function of a single organism, human or animal, of registering, retaining, recognizing, and recalling previous impressions and experiences. *Learning* simply means a modification of behavior in response to experience resulting from the acquisition and retention of abilities and their integration with some prior experience ("acquisition of a reaction potential" according to Hull[195]).

Without memory, therefore, there is no learning. Habits, skills, and attitudes are in general interpreted as processes included in the concept of learning. They are subject to disuse or reversal, to alteration and extinction, but usually they are not forgotten. As a matter of fact, not all that can be learned is subject to forgetting, even though whatever can be remembered can also be forgotten. In addition, not all that can be learned is subject to remembering. The wide area of overlapping between learning and remembering is not such, however, to maintain a firm distinction between the two processes from the psychological standpoint. The scope of learning, even though somewhat limited by man's biological equipment, is to contribute to spontaneous physical and psychological development and maturation and consequently, to the establishment of a continuously expanding behavior during lifetime. Even the manifestations of the genetically determined instinctual drives and the occasions for the triggering of reflex responses are remarkably subjected to learning experience.

The current trend in psychology, which is continuing the traditional direction taken by Ebbinghaus at the turn of the century, considers learning and memory as identical subjects. In experimental psychology the changes observed between a trial and the following one are interpreted as an expression of learning; the interval between the trials is studied as a manifestation of memory. Remembering and forgetting may also be considered behaviorally under learning because the latter applies to the acquisition of habits and to the content of memories as well. Since memories turn into habits by attaining autonomy, it is quite irrelevant to establish the exact timing of the process. There is no place in current psychological thinking, therefore, for the traditional distinction between memories manifested in ideation and habits expressed in behavior.

The intellectual function which accounts for the acquisition and retention of new abilities and their expression in new behavior is called *intelligence*. It is usually measured by intelligence tests, which however seem to measure only some adaptability that is biologically based. Talented as well as mentally retarded individuals are adequately screened with the aid of those tests. But when one tries to utilize the I.Q. test to establish what information-storing process is impaired and what can be done to cope with the inherent handicap, i.e. to evaluate the ability to learn for more appropriate teaching and educational methods, then that test does not respond fully to expectations since it does not inform of the several biological variations of normal learning abilities.

It seems that most of the knowledge of learning and memory is irrelevant as far as the capability to establish how and how much a child can learn and to predict further development of that potential is concerned. As a matter of fact, one may expect— and clinical evidence demonstrates it—several types of learning deficits in relation to several types of memory disturbance, such as the impairment of processing, retaining, and retrieving information. On the other hand, it has been shown that temporal lobe damage often does not affect the I.Q. and does not grossly change the normal intellectual appearance of the individual, but it still involves severe impairment of acquiring and retaining new information.[287b] Moreover, a number of children who show a normal I.Q. still have difficulty in acquiring and storing new information or cannot retrieve that which is already registered and permanently stored. On the other hand, it has been shown recently that the appropriate changes of the learning conditions may equalize the learning rate of low and high I.Q. children.[266] Differences in learning predicted on the basis of the I.Q. scores, therefore, may be eliminated just by modifying environmental factors, such as, for example, rearranging school environment to meet individual needs. As a matter of fact, when low I.Q. children are allowed longer intervals between the introduction of new information, their learning ability duplicates that of high I.Q. children who learn fast under normal school conditions.

The complexity of the learning process and the different quantitative parts played by the phases of memory account for the fact that the degree of functioning of these mental processes may not be equal. Classical is the case, for example, of the so-called memory prodigies who often are feebleminded, as well as that of the intellectually superior individuals whose memory abilities are often modest enough to justify a secondary role of memory in the development of their intelligence.[20]*

One of the most commonly used and traditionally studied types of learning is *learning by association* or *associative learning*. If a stimulus becomes associated with another one already fixated as a memory trace, there are more chances that it becomes a new memory. Despite some theoretical reserves, it has been recognized that the classical Aristotelian associationism is a valuable concept. The more similar the qualities of two stimuli are, the more meaningful the connections between them and easier the recall of the memory trace related to one of those stimuli, following the recall of the memory trace it has been associated with.**

---

*Retarded twins have been found to have an exceptional ability to memorize dates and calculate the calendar of thousands of years ago on the basis of a few data of present time. Mathematical prodigies, people who are particularly capable to recall numbers, at times up to fifty units, i.e. about seven times the numerical units which a person of average intelligence can recall (7 ± 2),[189, 260] were often rather dull persons. Other people, conversely, are gifted with an excellent memory but are so intelligent per se that memory contribution to their brightness appears as secondary. This is the case of the Italian humanist and philosopher Giovanni Pico, better known as Pico della Mirandola in his birthplace (16th century), the French physicist André Marie Ampère (16th-17th century), and the mathematicians Karl Friedrich Gauss (18th-19th century), from Germany, and Lenhard Euler (16th century), from Switzerland. Another type of hypermnesia is that which concerns words rather than numbers. In this respect, particular reputation was gained by the Italian bishop Gaspare Mezzofanti, who was recognized as able to speak forty-eight languages (dialects included).

**A more casual meaning of interconnections between different stimuli as a prerequisite for learning and memory has been emphasized by a more modern trend of associationism, which, however, is strongly contrasting to some basic concepts of *Gestalt psychology*. This trend of psychological thought has pointed to the natural tendency of establishing logical and meaningful connections between different experiential information and has considered memories as acting in constant communication with each other, thus indicating a sort of neural continuous activity as the basis for the retention process.

Gestalt psychology was initiated in Germany with Wertheimer[420] at the turn

The associative mechanism of brain functioning in man is easily exemplified by a person who may taste food just by looking at it or may imagine the appearance of someone just by hearing his voice. In animals, obviously, the only usable approach to the study of the associative mechanism of learning and memory is

---

of the century and continued with Koffka[235] and Köhler[233] in the United States. It maintains that sensations only account for the process of perception. Perception is more than a sum of sensations. Parts of a perceptual experience have a meaning only if considered in relation to their place in the whole (holistic approach to the psychological problems in contrast to the analytic approach of early schools).[426] The total "gestalt" or form or configuration, in the visual type of information and perception, comes first; the elements constituting the single object follow. An integrative process, involving selection, fusion, and elaboration, which transforms the mosaic of sensations into a "form," rather than casual association of simple, elementary sensations, is the prerequisite of the primary psychic experience allowing apperception and understanding of reality at the abstract level.

Gestalt psychology has also been very significant in making constructive criticism of another psychological approach, i.e. the so-called behaviorism or objective functionalism. Initiated in the United States by John B. Watson[417] at the turn of the century as a reaction to the introspective type of psychology, it has been developed and reelaborated in more recent times by a large number of psychologists with psychotherapeutical implications, too, particularly by B. F. Skinner[369] and O. H. Mowrer.[291] Behaviorists see the study of behavior and the objective approach to psychological problems as the way to overcome the bias of an early conception dating back to the French philosopher René Descartes (16th-17th century), a conception which put the emphasis on self-observation and analysis (introspection), rather than on the objectification of reality.

The development of behaviorism was favored by the contemporary neurophysiological trend of research on conditioned reflexes initiated in Russia by I. P. von Pavlov[312] and V. M. von Bechterev.[29] Finally, the extreme was reached, i.e. considering the behavior of animals and human beings as a "bundle of reflexes." This was particularly antagonized by gestalt psychology, which, in turn, has offered unsatisfactory interpretation, from the neurophysiological point of view, of the mode in which perception becomes apperception. In psychophysiology of vision, for example, the recognition of a square or a circle was considered a result of the establishment of a specific pattern of neuronal excitation topographically corresponding to the specific form or configuration of the perceived object. It is difficult to understand, however, how the cortical activity corresponding to the process described by gestalt psychology becomes consciously intelligible. As a matter of fact, nonproprioceptive properties have been recognized in the cerebral cortex.[60 a-c, e, f] A more sound neurophysiological explanation of the brain mechanics which may account eventually for the integration of the discrepancies between some concepts of behaviorism and those of gestalt psychology has been offered by the Italian neurologist V. M. Buscaino[60 a-l] and his school in Italy. (See Chapter III.)

the indirect one which utilizes the classical conditioning method based on Sherrington's stimulus-response model of spinal reflexes.[365] The Russian school of neurophysiology took that approach at the beginning of the century. A conditioned reflex, or better, a conditioned response,[110] can be interpreted as a particular, privileged case of associative mechanism. To account for acquired behavior, von Pavlov postulated the establishment of new connections between neurons after birth and as a consequence of experience. These connections, however, were never experimentally demonstrated. (See Chapter II.) Von Pavlov's classical experiment on a dog responding with salivation (conditioned response) to a sound of a bell or to a light (conditioned stimulus), after having associated it with an unconditioned one (administration of food), has shown that it is possible to elicit learning and memory and to cause, therefore, a given behavior by the so-called classical conditioning.[312] The contiguity between the two stimuli, which is fundamental in classical conditioning, is an important but still an insufficient factor, even if combined with reinforcement, for making a response connected with a stimulus.

Perceptual learning and *learning by observation or imitation* must precede conditioning. A number of innate sensory-motor connections, finally, play a significant role in the process. A recent experiment by Garcia and Ervin[139] indicates that the organism is endowed with a high degree of built-in specificity of response. Perceptual learning results from the disentangling of a stimulus from the environment through perceptual differentiation and categorization based on previous learning. Learning by observation or imitation is self-explanatory and is supported by numerous animal studies.*

---

*In Snygg's experiments,[372] twenty-nine trials were required with rats which learned a Warden U-maze with ten choice points. When five of the correct turns were painted white, the mean dropped to twelve. When the incorrect paths were painted black, the mean dropped again to seven. In Schaeffer's experiments,[355] rats kept in restraining cages were moved bodily over the correct pathways in a Y-maze into a white or black alley, and they were fed there. Thirteen of seventeen rats chose the correct turns. Undoubtedly, associative phenomena may be operating in those experiments in addition to observation, but certainly when rats break up a total maze path into submazes and show anticipatory movements as

Von Pavlov's experiments on animals[312] and those by von Bechterev on humans[28] have stimulated numerous investigators to work on conditioning procedures and to study their effects on learning and memory. In man the classical conditioning does not necessarily follow the typical reinforcement of a positive response by reward. Eyelid closure or hand withdrawal in response to a stimulus originally neutral paired with an electric shock in one case and with an air puff in the other case are experimental examples of this type of conditioning. Pavlovian conditioning may account for the development of neurotic symptoms, especially phobias or nail biting, and their persisting despite their maladaptive function. It may also account for the other type of learning called *maladaptive learning*, well exemplified by blushing and asthmatic attacks. In the laboratory, on the other hand, experimental neuroses were initially caused by von Pavlov by requiring the animals to make the appropriate conditioned response to stimuli of increasingly difficult perceptual discrimination. Conditioning type of learning is a sort of blind learning because it leads to the acquisition of uneffective behavior. But *motor learning* (learning motor skills), such as walking, or *rule learning*, such as acquiring those fundamental rules by which the subject becomes able to generate a variety of acts, from motor skills to sentence structure, are exceptional examples of a blind type of learning producing effective behavior rather than simply producing the capacity of modifying it according to the situation.

One of the most significant contributions of von Pavlov and von Bechterev's studies on conditioning was the demonstration that it is possible to elicit some other forms of conditioned

---

if they had ideas of "ahead" and "around" the corner, as Snygg also noted, associational factors appear to be out of the picture.

Other investigators[70, 213] have shown that learning by observation is more efficient than the method of conventional shaping procedures. More recently, Chesler[70] has shown that maternal influence improves learning by observation. Kittens, observing their mothers perform a stimulus-controlled response (lever pressing to a visual stimulus for food), acquired and discriminated that response sooner than kittens observing a strange female cat performance. Initial differences in attentiveness to demonstrator performances disappeared by the second day. Both mothers and stranger demonstrators showed a clear attitude for different types of social behavior, the altruistic ones (food sharing, for example) included.

behavior, which appear to be more directly responsible for voluntary acts, as the classical type of conditioning has been recognized to be for involuntary acts. Originated by Skinner[369] in 1938 and called *operant conditioning,* it is characterized by the fact that the conditioned response is an apparently spontaneous one, i.e. it is not elicited by the experimenter. In *instrumental conditioning* the response allows the animal to achieve some result, such as avoiding punishment or getting reward: in the former case, the response is known as avoidance response (pulling a limb to avoid a shock, for example); in the latter case, the response is known as reward response (pressing a lever to get a food pellet, for example). Instrumental conditioning in man represents more a test of perceptual discrimination or of problem solving than a simplified type of learning. As a matter of fact, the performer should master efficiently the nonlearning component of the task to make the performance satisfactory, while animals should only discover certain conditions or cues of the experimental situation which contribute to the success of the performance, such as a light being on or off, or a given time having been elapsed since the last reinforcing event.

In the learning process accomplished through instrumental conditioning, the reward is more effective as a spur than as a punishment. This is the same as saying that the extinction of one response and its replacement with a different one is elicited more by the pleasure of reward than by the pain of the punishment. The latter still has a useful feedback function, since it may cause a temporary suppression of habits rather than their true unlearning. The rewarded behavior will eventually substitute that for which the learner was punished when the punishment stimulated him to try an alternative behavior. Punishment, unquestionably, can either facilitate or retard the performance of a learned behavior according to the mode in which it is used in a given situation.[65] When instinctive rather than learned behavior is punished, stereotyped or neurotic behavior usually occurs.[189] On the other hand, it has been shown that punishment can be used effectively to suppress learned behavior without any concomitant deleterious side effects. Karsh[221] very recently has provided evidence that persevering behavior develops in rats following punishment combined with reward in a learning situation. All rats, given a choice between a rewarded alternative and a conflict alternative (rewarded and punished), developed position fixations (persevering position responses) when the position of the alternatives was reversed. All animals given one rewarded (or punished and non-rewarded) alternative, conversely, learned to choose the rewarded side during twenty-five successive reversals. The occurrence of fixated behavior in the conflict-reversal situation, therefore, is considerably greater than the position preference that would occur without punishment. Since other groups of rats reversed normally, the extremely fixated behavior may result from the conflict situation. It seems clear that this fixated behavior, i.e. the choice to endure conflict and punishment when they could be easily avoided by the choice of a rewarded alternative, cannot be predicted on the basis of the current understanding of the role of reinforcement and conflict in the learning process.[232]

The time-honored method of *learning by trial and error* is, in terms of conditioning, a method in which the conditioned response precedes the conditioned stimulus. Experimentally, the animal does a number of casual movements within the "problem cages," as Thorndike[402] called them, which are gradually eliminated to lead to a more adequate and direct behavior. The number of errors which an animal makes to find the exit of a maze where a reward is located (food, for example) decreases after each trial until the solution is found, learned, and memorized. At this point the animal knows how to behave to reach the goal.

Learning by insight represents the highest form of learning as learning by trial and error represents the lowest one as far as the quality of learning is concerned. It involves the grasping of meaningful relationships between things which not only have an occasional and immediate value in problem solving, but may be utilized anytime at an abstract level for the solution of problems of similar type.

A basic difference between classical conditioning and the other forms of conditioning procedures believed to be responsible for voluntary behavior is that in classical conditioning the reinforcement process or reward is limited by the unconditioned stimulus already eliciting the response to be learned and that, conversely, in operant and instrumental conditioning the reward is unlimited and has the property of reinforcing not only the stimulus eliciting the specific response, but also any immediately preceding response. Thus, any given response may be strengthened by any different reward.

One of the implications of considering operant and instrumental conditioning superior to classical conditioning because they are able to influence behavior rather than simply involuntary acts, as in von Pavlov and von Bechterev's type of conditioning, is the fact that those types of conditioning and learning involve only voluntary, muscular responses controlled by the central nervous system, rather than involuntary, visceral, and emotional responses controlled by the autonomic nervous system,[227] as in classical conditioning. Perhaps this implication also stems from the traditional belief in the "superiority" of "reason" and voluntary skeletal responses over emotions and presumably over involuntary visceral responses: superior soul located in the head vs inferior soul located in the body, according to Plato's philosophy; cerebrospinal nervous system of the great brain and spinal cord vs "little brains" represented by the vegetative ganglionic system along the spinal cord, controlling visceral responses, according to Bishat's neuronanatomical and physiological work; inability of sympathetic nerves to perform finely differentiated individual responses, such as those assured by central nervous system fiber, according to Cannon's physiological studies; the hysterical-like symptoms controlled by the central nervous system in a rather symbolic way vs the psychosomatic symptoms controlled by the autonomic nervous system and interpreted as the psychological expression of the individual's emotional state in psychiatric patients.[285]

One can understand how it has been officially stated[229] that "for automatically mediated behavior, the evidence points unequivocally to the conclusion that such visceral and emotional responses can be modified by classical, but not instrumental training method." As N. E. Miller[285] has recently pointed out, such evidence ". . . consists only of failure to secure instrumental learning in two incompletely reported exploratory experiments and a vague allusions to the Russian literature.[291, 369] It is only against a cultural background of great prejudice that such weak evidence could lead to such a strong conviction." That instrumental learning can modify only responses controlled by the central nervous system, and classical conditioning, only responses controlled by the autonomic nervous system is not an absolutely accepted fact; that the implication of the concept that instrumental and classical learning are two distinct phenomena rather than different manifestations of the same process is not absolutely true seems to be supported by a group of experimental data obtained by N. E. Miller *et al.* over the past ten years at Rockefeller University of New York.

Three decades ago N. E. Miller noted similarities between the laws of the classical and instrumental conditioning and learning. He hypothesized that only one type of learning really exists and that specific conditions of the learning situation influence the specific details of the learning process during the conditioning procedures. The total evidence of the experimental data obtained by Miller and co-workers seems to support the assumption mentioned before. As a matter of fact, instrumental learning techniques have been shown by those authors to cause the learning of any visceral response which could be acquired through classical conditioning. This disproves the traditional concept that the autonomic, vegetative, or involuntary nervous system is inferior to the voluntary central nervous system.

Before discussing the implications of this research not only for the theory of learning, but also for the cause and treatment of psychosomatic symptoms and in general for the understanding of normal homeostasis, a representative, typical experiment of the series carried out by Miller *et al.* deserves discussion. Rats were temporarily paralyzed with curare (1.2 mg/kg as a starting dose and continuous intraperitoneal infusion of additional amounts of the same dose per hour for the entire duration of the experiment) in order to rule out any interference of muscular contraction upon heart function. Heart rate was recorded continuously by the electrocardiograph wired to the reward device. Artificial respiration and curarization were adjusted to keep the heart rate of the 500-gm control animal constant and also to maintain body temperature, peripheral vasomotor responses, and pCO_2 of the blood steady. Animals were trained to increase or decrease the heart rate by rewarding them through electrical stimulation of the rewarding center of the brain. By using the "technique of shaping," i.e. by immediately rewarding first very small and frequently occurring changes in the correct direction of the heart rate and then progressively larger changes as the criterion for reward, changes averaging twenty per cent in either direction were obtained within ninety minutes. The animals so trained showed good retention of the learned task.

Other similar experiments by Miller *et al.* have demonstrated that laboratory animals can learn to control the rate of production of saliva and urine, to raise or lower blood pressure, to increase or decrease gastrointestinal contractions and blood flow through the walls of the stomach and peripheral blood vessels, and also to change the pattern of the electroencephalographic recording.

Significant implications of this research on the learning process of visceral and glandular responses and its basic achievement, i.e. the demonstration that the autonomic nervous system can also learn through reward and punishment, are the following: all types of learning can be interpreted as manifestations of a unique process; the autonomic nervous system is not inferior to the central nervous system; there are no reasons for considering operant or instrumental learning responsible only for behavior; finally, it is possible to learn to control visceral and emotional responses by rewarding for doing so or by punishing for not doing so.

Implications of more practical value are those which concern the possibility of training human beings presenting psychophysiological signs or symptoms to control them by reward and punishment. The first positive results obtained in patients motivated to slow their tachycardia or decrease their hypertension and trained to do so by instrumental conditioning (when the heart rate or the blood pressure values decrease, the patient hears a beep which he learns to keep on as long as possible) encourage the investigation in patients who must learn to control changes of peripheral blood flow, gastric secretion, electroencephalographic patterns, and other nonvoluntary functions. There is no question, however, that the results of this type of investigation are biased by the fact that by using in man the same rigorous controls applied to animals, curarization primarily, it is possible that the unconscious learning of those selected responses which can cause visceral reactions interferes with the responses mediated by the autonomic nervous system. This difficulty, however, may be overcome by developing more ingenious control of body functions so that the specificity of the visceral change obtained can be properly assured. Curarization, for example, may find a substitute in hypnotic suggestion. In addition, physical or psychological relaxation by breathing regularly may help in working with human beings.

It is certainly interesting, on the basis of the experimental data discussed above, that psychosomatic symptoms may be seen under different perspectives with respect to the hysterical type of symptoms, the former being controlled by the autonomous nervous system; the latter, by the central nervous system. If instrumental conditioning, which was thought to be effective on voluntary functions controlled by the central nervous system, is effective in eliciting learning of visceral responses, then there is no reason to make a differentiation between the former and the latter. In addition, various conditions of learning may account for some individual differences in the pattern of the autonomic response, partially related to cultural and social factors, partially born with the individual.

From the practical viewpoint, instrumental learning may be used for controlling any functional or organic sign or symptom under the domain of the central or autonomic nervous system, which is expected to change direction by other medical procedures, but which practically fails to respond to drugs or cannot be treated with them for some pathophysiological reasons, and which finally can be continuously monitored technically. Encouraging results have been obtained by applying instrumental training in subjects with organic cardiac arrythmias or epilepsy. Attempts have been and are being made to treat insomnia by rewarding a high voltage electroencephalogram. Other prospective candidates for instrumental learning are individuals with hypertension (not related to kidney pathology), asthma, spastic colitis, gastric ulcer, and migraine. That a human being can learn by reward or punishment, just as a dog does, i.e. by instrumental conditioning, is a well-documented fact. It needs, however, further confirmation and should be studied more from the viewpoint of the practical implications.

A fundamental contribution to the *development of learning* has been given over the past four decades by the Swiss psychologist Jean Piaget on the basis of careful observation and genial conceptualization of the behavior of children as representative of the modes and ways in which they learn.[114, 323] Even lacking scientific rigor, Piaget's method of study has led him to original ideas which have been confirmed by younger and more sophisticated investigators all over the world. The basic points of Piaget's contribution to a general theory of developmental stages of intelligence can be synthetized in the concept that adaptive thinking and behavior develop in a sequence of stages in relationship to physical age. Such stages see the development of new mental abilities, which also characterize, by setting limits, what can be learned during that period of time. They will be dependent both upon the genetical characteristics of the individual and the influence of environmental factors on that natural material.

The Piagetian nature and nurture theory of the development of human intelligence basically contrasts to the Brunerian theory that "any subject can be taught effectively in some intellectual honest form to any child at any stage of development." The first stage or sensori-motor period, from birth to the second year, is characterized by the evolution of those abilities which are necessary to construct and reconstruct objects. The second stage, or preoperational period, from second to seventh year, is characterized by the elaboration of the symbolic function, i.e. of those abilities which are essential for reproducing things. The language is acquired; dreams, symbolic play, drawing, and graphic representation appear. The third stage, or concrete operational period, from the seventh to the eleventh year, is characterized by internalized actions or concrete operations which allow one to think about things. The fourth stage, or formal operational period, from twelfth year to the fifteenth year, is characterized by formal operations which allow one to think about his own thoughts, to reason realistically and about contrary-to-fact propositions, to understand metaphor, and to build up ideals for the future. In the late adolescence and adulthood, finally, the intellectual development is completed, and only wisdom gradually increases with experience.

The American psychologist Jerome Bruner,[54 a] more than criticizing Piaget's apparently casual methodology of study, has argued about some of Piaget's interpretations of the phenomena observed. For example, as far as the problem of change and conservation of child thinking is concerned, Bruner believes that the syntactical rules of language rather than the logic can account for the child's discovery that a quantity of orangeade, poured into different containers so that its quantity appears more or less, remains unchanged despite the apparent modification of its volume. Thus, according to Bruner, it seems that some internalized verbal formula rather than any rational operation of the mind shields the child from the overpowering appearance of visual displays.

Piaget's contribution to the development of intelligence has had and is having a remarkable and important impact in the field of education. As a matter of fact, the most relevant discoveries made by Piaget in the past decades, during which he studied particularly the development of those mental abilities of children and adolescents which gradually enable them to construct a view of the world in conformance with reality as seen by the adult, are the following: first, the fact that the child copes with change by distinguishing permanence from transformation, not simply by objective appearance of reality, but through the power of his reason; second, that children, during elementary school at the age of seven, use a reasoning ability which is limited with respect to that of older children, adolescents, and adults in the fact that it deals with concrete things rather than with verbal propositions.

The educational implications are self-evident. As a matter of fact, as far as the first discovery is concerned, children receive a type of education tending to focus upon the static aspects of reality rather than upon its dynamic transformations. Despite the fact that children are continuously exposed to changes and transformations of reality because of their physical changes, too they are taught about what and how things are and not under what conditions things remain the same or change. Since children, as Piaget has pointed out, discover changes as well as permanence or conservation of reality by the force of their own logic, rather than by simply having a mirror image of the world, education should deal more with the modes and ways in which changes in reality occur.

As far as Piaget's second important discovery is concerned, elementary education should not overemphasize the use of verbal propositions. The reasoning ability of elementary school children at the age of six or seven years is not similar to that of adults, thus requiring verbal education at a level appropriate to their level of intellectual ability. In Piaget's theory of intellectual development, language and thoughts are closely related, but they are still different systems. Particular forms of environmental stimulation may influence language to a greater extent than thoughts. The verbal facility of middle class children may be misleading as far as teaching is concerned; it falsely indicates that they understand more than they really do. Conversely, the language retarded development of inner-city Negro children may mislead about their mental ability, which is certainly greater than that which one would expect from their verbalization, especially at the age at which concrete operations are attained (7-11 years). Attempts to teach those children concrete operations have been unsuccessful. These substantiating operations are still dependent upon the environment, as is language, but develop in a longer time and require a wider variety of environmental stimulation.

Another aspect of Piaget's contribution to the development of intelligence, which is significant with respect to its bearing on education, is, assuming that there are stages of intellectual development related to age, the question of whether those stages can be accelerated and to what extent. Piaget's conviction based on his observations is that there is an optimal time for the organization of operations and that this time varies from individual to individual and with the subject matter. While future research should clarify what this optimal time is in most cases, the present educational attitude should be that of a moderate acceleration of child intelligence and the avoidance of reaching maximal values in order to prevent the development of intelligence from not reaching the expected levels after an initial attainment. An accepted concept, however, is that an early learning is more durable, since in the first decade of life the human being learns more and faster than at any other mental and physical age.

The overall impact of Piaget's theory of intellectual development upon education is certainly positive. The tests he has proposed are widely used, and new curricula are being prepared on the basis of his findings about children's understanding of scientific and mathematical concepts; last, but not least, the changing attitude of teachers and educators in operating with the human goal of ". . . creating men who are capable of doing new things, not simply of repeating what the generations have done—men who are creative, inventive, and discoverers."[114]

Memory, as the mental ability of retaining and reviving impressions or of recognizing and recalling previous experiences in the same form in which they took place and in relationship to the same cues with which they were learned, consists of three phases, fundamentally different as far as the characteristics and mechanisms of production are concerned: an initial phase of registration (or coding) of the incoming stimuli; a second phase of retention (or storage) of perceptual and nonperceptual registered information; a third phase of recall (or retrieval) of the information already or not yet stored in a permanent form. The term "memory" is more specific for the second phase of retention or storage. Remembering—and its opposite, i.e. forgetting—are also used as less scientific terms to indicate the outcome of the retrieval phase of memory.

1. The *registration phase* of memory consists of a process which registers the incoming information not only in form of simple percepts, but also in form of concepts, abstractions, and unconscious or subliminal impressions in a way that it can be permanently stored and adequately retrieved when needed in a form similar to that of the initial registration. *Short-term memory* and *intermediate memory* (see pages 38, 87) indicate registration and retention of information over different time intervals following the initial impression of the activity trace. Short-term memory occupies a few minutes up to thirty minutes after the learning trial,[51, 144a-c, 237a-c, 327, 329] but it could last several hours[17] or even days.[56] *Immediate memory* lasts a few seconds up to one minute in figural information. In man it is tested by repeating digits and finishing sentences.

Only a limited number of perceptions is transformed as an organized pattern into memories, and only a fraction of them, which are capable of being impressed as memories, is actually perceived by the sense organs; perceptions occurs primarily in relationship to a selective constructiveness due to interest and motivation. Thus, one does not remember all that is perceived, and even those perceptions which had a lasting effect on behavior are subject to forgetting.

As far as the most usual situation of perceptual information is concerned, memory registration first requires the appropriate elaboration of percepts, i.e. a complex process of simplification (omission of unimportant details and emphasis on the important ones), revision and modification of the content in relation to its type and general interest, specific motivation, and plans for further action. If it is true that a single exposure is sufficient for the registration of percepts and for learning, it is also proved that some experiential information is registered only after repeated presentation (role of *repetition* in learning and importance of *rehearsal* as a technique for learning). One could speculate, therefore, that incremental or latent learning precedes at times the phase of registration. In contrast to information provided through sensory channels, such as vision, olfaction, and touch, that provided by kinesthetic and proprioceptive modalities may be facilitated in being registered and stored by covert rehearsal.

That registration is a fundamental process of memory is also supported by the fact that in several clinical manifestations of memory impairment the deficit is in the perceptive phase. (See pages 40, 42, 43.) In the case of nonrecognition of a figure, for example, even after a few seconds from its initial presentation, any interference being absent, the defect is in the short-term memory mechanism. On the other hand, information which is still out of the storage system as a memory trace may be available immediately for retrieval. In general, *spontaneous decay* and *decay due to interference* are recognized as responsible for short-term memory deterioration.[292, 319] The functional role of this deterioration is that of preserving temporarily a given information which will not be utilized in the very near future, so avoiding the storage of superfluous information in the brain. Underwood's experiments[410] indicate that efficient learners are also efficient forgetters. The ability to memorize, in other words, can be limited to the ability to retain information just for a short period of time (for example, just for a lecture). The speculation arises that some instruction about the length of time in which an information must be retained should be included in the process of memory registration. Underwood's trained learners performed better than untrained subjects in a test of immediate recall on nonsense syllables, but they remembered less than the naive learners at twenty-four hours time interval from the trial.

Thus, repetition, rehearsal, and interest, as well as spontaneous decay and decay due to interference, but in the opposite direction, play an important part in the process of memory registration and in preparing the traces to become permanent. A quite significant contribution to the acquisition of memories is also given by the *unpredictable character of the information*. The significance of the anticipation is that it is an unfavorable factor for the registration and retention of memories. The smaller the expectancy of new information as able to match some model previously formed in the brain, the higher the strength of the ability of memorizing it. The anticipated detailed significance of an event, in other words, is indirectly related to the ability of that event to become an endurable memory trace. Interest and expectation, however, are relevant in the process of filing the new information and matching it against some previous model with the purpose of an easier retrieval.

From a strictly psychological point of view and as reconstructed from its effects and from brain defects associated with memory impairment, the process of memory registration appears to consist of selection and cross-indexing of information according to several principles, the most common of which are temporal and spatial (along the length) contiguity, hierarchical organization, preestablished patterning, and schematization as well as presence of innate associations at perceptual and conceptual levels (Jungian archetypal symbols[217]) so that the information becomes easily accessible and retrievable. Learning experiments with the so-called paired-associate technique have shown that verbal or pictorial *mediators* play an essential role in the establishment of a stronger memory trace. Some mediators, however, fit better than others to a given subject. Images are more effective in favoring initial associations; verbal mediators and mnemonic tricks are preferred by older people, who conversely are less apt to resort to mediators spontaneously than young adults.[194] Free environmental experience, especially early visual and motor stimuli, have been recognized as being of basic importance in the establishment of *learning by imprinting* in several animals, but particularly in birds.[370]

Transformation and coding are the two other basic modalities by which information becomes registered in the memory system. They are particularly valuable in the case of perceptual and concrete information obtained from the sensory organs because of the difficulty in recording this information isomorphically, and they are essential in the case of abstract and conceptual information. Condensation, reduction, and grouping the data represent some of the most common ways in which the coding process takes place. Transformations, together with units, classes, systems, relations, and implications, represent the six *products of information* in Guilford's structure of the intellect model.[166]* Product of information represents the abstract mode in which the concrete information resulting from learning experience is registered and permanently stored in the brain to form human knowledge. Transformations are changes, revisions, redefinitions, or modifications by which any product of information goes from one state to another. They have a well-documented effect of enhancing retention. Their complexity and the attention which they require make the memory trace more durable and its retrieval more accurate up to a point beyond which errors become more numerous because of the alteration of the information necessary to fit it within preexisting schemata.

Implications are concepts which are expected or predicted from a given information. Units seem to be retained better within classes and systems. Some input are motor patterns, plan strategies, tactics, methods, and programs. A simple form in which information is conceived is units, or things to which names are applied. Class is a set of objects with one or more common properties. Relations, usually expressed by propositions, are types of connections between two things. Systems are complex patterns or organizations of independent or interacting parts (mathematical equations, plans, programs, and outlines).

2. *The retention (or storage) phase of memory* consists of a process occurring between the acquisition and registration of information and its recognition and retrieval, which makes the memory trace, especially if isolated, resistant to erasure, durable, and permanent, even though susceptible to lawful changes because of experience. While the finite events of acquisition and recall of information or learning and exercising a skill are susceptible to erasure and seen as resulting from an ongoing process in the brain, the retention phase of memory is considered as a

---

*In the structure of the intellect model, which is an operational model, the parameters are the product of information, content, and operations. The latter include evaluation, convergent and divergent production, cognition, and memory. Cybernetic organization and computer functioning represent more sophisticated operational models in which the events are conceived in terms of interconnected series of transmissions of information.

noncontinuous, even a noninert process (See Chapter III.) in contrast to an earlier interpretation based on *Ribot's first law of regression*. Ribot[341] emphasized the extension of memory impairment from recent to more distant and then, remote events. As a matter of fact, most deficits of memory function are characterized by the fact that older memories are retained better than the more recent ones. On the basis of Ribot's first law of regression and on the assumption that retention expresses more a static than a dynamic process, one would expect that older memories outlast the recent ones.

It is known today that a process of *consolidation* is required between the registration phase, during which the memory trace is labile and vulnerable and therefore subject to decay, and the phase of retrieval of the stabilized and stored trace to make the permanent retention possible. Its basic operations consist of cross-filing and embedding new information with information already stored, with consequent gradual modification of the original information to fit into preexisting schemata, as the classical Bartlett's serial reproduction experiments have shown.[26] Retention of memory cannot be imagined, therefore, as occurring according to the simple mechanism of imprinting of the memory trace on a wax tablet which Plato envisaged so long ago. Called *trace model of memory* in more recent times and having given the first simple explanation of the process of forgetting, i.e. the spontaneous decay of the memory trace, it was reelaborated on two decades ago in the *dual-trace model of memory*. It will be discussed in detail in Chapter III. Here it should be anticipated that the model is based on a strictly neurophysiological interpretation of the mechanism of memory registration and consolidation in the sense that these memory phases would result from an electrical, continuously ongoing process which promotes structural changes in the neuronal network of the brain tissue involved, so accounting for the permanent stability of the memory trace.

3. The *recall (or retrieval) phase of memory* consists of a complex and still partially clear process which allows the recollection of previously acquired and permanently—and also nonpermanently—stored information in the same form and in relationship with

the same cues with which it was learned. Verbal recall, which is the most typical type of recall, does not require the overt performance of a behavioral act, but just the vocal recollection of a memory. Operational recall, on the other hand, may be either fortuitous or deliberate, respectively, if the performance takes place under the influence of an implicit contextual cue or is a specific response to a contextual stimulus or question. The retrieval of information, therefore, while possibly irrelevant or incorrect in response to that explicit stimulus or question, can be relevant to the total situation and therefore important for problem solving.

An alternate, even less demanding, process of remembering is *recognition,* which operates in the recall of information registered through certain senses, such as sight, touch, or olfaction. Visual images are easily retrieved, and in this case necessary recollection depends on thoughts based on those images rather than on words, such as a philosophical concept, a moral law, a mathematical equation, and even psychic elaborations occurring during sleep and due to unconscious cerebration (verbal thinking). The process of recognition, however, is implicit within the general concept of recall and has been hypothesized as resulting from a sort of scanning activity in the relevant memory files and from sorting out, ordering, and patterning the suitable entries with the aid of a search model (the "address of information" in computer terminology). The higher the signal property of a memory, the more numerous are the chances to search the memory trace during the process of recall. An unsatisfactory level of discrimination or the inability to perceive destructive cues may explain the error in matching the content of recall to the object of the search process. Particularly significant in this process are some *strategies,* such as those which limit the load of information needed for progress in the search with resulting elimination of duplications, thus avoiding or reducing interference and increasing the enrichment of information generated by the search process.

Recall is based on two fundamental operations: divergent and convergent production. *Divergent production* generates local possibilities because of the variety of the output derived from the same source of information. *Convergent production* generates local necessities, and deductions are the end result. It is also characterized by a limited output and a narrow research because of the many restrictions. An example of convergent production is given by a person who memorizes a complete syllogism (with the premises and conclusions) and who is able to reach the correct conclusion if offered two other premises completely unknown to him and unrelated to the original premises. Since the cue statements are new for that particular item of information, transfer recall mechanism seems to be involved in the process, especially in divergent production.

Recall may occur at different levels of abstraction. It can also be partial or total. A relationship between those concepts seems to exist in the sense that when an analytic and abstractive method of information processing is acquired, then the *eidetic imagery,* i.e. the ability to reproduce in detail on a blank screen a picture after its removal from the view, is lost. As a matter of fact, that ability is seen very often in children, while adults, who are not supposed to think only concretely, are still able to learn in rote fashion and to recall verbatim, although they usually learn and remember in an abstract way. Total recall in such a case is exceptional, and it has its roots in a defective sorting out, editing, and integrating the mnemonic material to be retrieved. The concept of partial recall, for its part, is not simply the specular image of the concept of total recall. It simply means that in the process of reconstruction from well-retained memory traces, information is partially forgotten throughout a rapid decay of traces or most often through the mechanisms of response interference or retroactive interference, which will be discussed below. Thus, the recall is partial.

Attention, relaxation, reduction of the evaluative operation (the so-called suspended judgment indicated by Osborn[304]), completeness of investigating situation, overlearning, and recency of practice as well as interest, attitude, and emotional involvement are factors which operate very significantly in the process of recall.

If the model of comparator mechanisms based on a scanning

operation satisfies the requirement of the recognition of perfect identities, it certainly does not account for the recognition of partial and imperfect identities or of the similarity between things apparently different and for the bisociative process underlying intellectual qualities, such as creativeness.[234] The reconstructive character of recall may be better understood by considering that an associative mechanism is involved in the process of gathering the mnemonic material for the act of recall. Associations operating in one occasion, however, while predetermined by what happened during registration and possibly during retention in immediate recall and in rote learning, are not so in delayed recall, especially in the case of retrieval of abstract information and of material representative of remote past as seen at that particular moment.

The recall phase of memory is that in which most *forgetting* occurs, as resulting from several types of interference[297, 318, 319, 410, 430] and from failure in the searching operations. Forgetting may also result from spontaneous decay of the memory trace, in which case it is more closely related to the process of consolidation than to that of the initial registration or the final recall. If resulting from spontaneous decay, forgetting in general expresses a real loss of the memory trace *(memory erasure)* rather than a partial or total, temporary or permanent failure to retrieve information. Decay resulting from interference is also a frequent cause of transient or durable forgetting. The types of interference most clearly understood are the retroactive, the proactive, and the response-interference.

Retroactive interference (or inhibition) is that exerted by a material learned after the acquisition of the unavailable memory trace. The learning of one problem may impair the retention of a previously learned problem. The effect is particularly evident on poorly articulated and codable information in the continuous process of schematization, especially if followed by closely similar but different information.[292] The more recently acquired information competes with the earlier information and prevails over it.[430] The process, obviously, does not occur during the registration phase of memory, but rather during the retention phase, in which phase it may be a cause of unlearning, and during its implicit and unobservable recall. The retroactive interference which originates in the phase of overt recall, with resulting failure of retrieving an earlier and permanent memory trace, is called *response-interference*. Its effect is temporary in contrast to the permanent effect occurring when the same source of interference is operating in the rehearsal of a message in the phase of registration.

Proactive interference (or inhibition) is that exerted by a material learned before the acquisition of the unavailable memory trace. The learning of one problem may impair the retention of a subsequently learned problem. Considered as less important than the retroactive type, it has been shown more recently to be fundamental in rote learning, i.e. learning and memorizing verbatim a list of unconnected words.[410] In this particular type of learning, which concerns human learning occurring in life situations, the inhibitory effect seems to take place by reducing the increment from the proactive facilitatory effect of the information previously acquired on further learning (*proactive facilitation*). The transformation of the early learning of childhood, established basically through the formation of new associations, into the adult type of learning, established through transfer learning, the acquisition of new information on the basis of the initial information, the recombination and subdivision of previously established associations, and the development of schemata, results essentially from proactive facilitation.*

---

*Proactive interference has been also demonstrated in mammals (rat) and birds (pigeon) but not in the goldfish. In a recent experiment by Behrend *et al.*[30] retention in the pigeon and the goldfish was measured one day or two weeks after the mastery of each of a series of color discriminations. The amount of forgetting increased with the number of prior problems and increased more rapidly at longer, rather than shorter, intervals. The amount of forgetting in the goldfish, conversely, was independent, at both intervals, of the number of prior problems. These results appear suggestive of different memory mechanisms in the pigeon and the goldfish. To quote Behrend *et al.*: "When a color preference is established and reversed in a pigeon, traces of the original training apparently remain after reversal training to interfere with the traces of that training and of subsequent training. Ablation experiments suggest that the hyperstriatum of the pigeon plays a part in the storage of these traces (Powers, A. S., Dissertation, Bryn Mawr College, 1968). After the reversal performance of a pigeon has been improved by training in a series of problems, injury to the hyperstriatum produces better reten-

The fact that most of the time forgetting is only temporary, thus not expressing any real loss of the memory trace, has led to the concept that any learning experience is never completely lost, as pointed out first by Freud in 1900.[134a-c] This concept, however, seems to contrast to the fact that some memories are acquired at the implicit or explicit condition that they should be lost or should undergo such a change during the process of schematization, so that they can be practically considered as missed as original memory traces. If psychoanalysis has shown through different techniques that forgotten memories, especially initial perceptions free from subsequent accretion and available only in dreams, in hallucinatory experience, or in abnormal verbal behavior (such as slips of tongue), may be recollected for therapeutic purpose, then psychoanalysis, conversely, has not proved that that which is learned is never lost. Freud, himself, in 1930 modified his concept of memory developed three decades earlier in the sense that nothing that was in the mind need ever perish. Psychoanalytic theory has pointed to *repression* and to similar mental mechanisms of defense, such as denial and isolation, as being responsible for unconscious warding off from the sphere of awareness of memories associated with sexual and aggressive impulses operating during childhood, with the purpose of protecting the individual from the anxiety which would be aroused if these were admitted into consciousness.

Repression, however, expresses not only an unconscious mechanism of defense of ego function. Being at the basis of forgetting, it may also express a motivated act rather than an automatic act of forgetting, and in that case, it is better indicated as active or conscious *suppression*. Its purpose is to exclude from consciousness painful memories and to protect the individual from thoughts

---

tion of a preference established after operation and makes reversal difficult once more. One way to explain the fish results is to assume that, when a preference is reversed in a fish, the effects of the original training are not stored independently after reversal, but supplanted entirely by those of the reversal training. The progressive improvement in habit reversal which appears in the fish after enlargement of the optic tectum by transplantation (Bresler, D. E. and Bitterman, M. E., *Science, 163:*590, 1969) may be due to enhanced capacity for storage and the consequent opportunity for interference."

which may shatter his self-image and hopes, thus cooperating in the long run to survival. Suppression, however, may be also seen more simply as a constituent of normal function, valuable in the process of learning and remembering, i.e. *learning not to remember*. A defective mechanism of recall seems to be responsible for this type of forgetting.[330e]

If repression is partial and the residual anxiety-provoking memories have an alternate outlet in symptom formation when they reach the realm of conscious awareness, then a neurotic state may rise. Psychoanalysis as a therapeutic technique (through free association, dream analysis, hypnosis, etc.) may be instrumental in bringing totally into consciousness the incompletely repressed memories (this effect is known as *catharsis*) in order that they be dealt with in a rational rather than in a neurotic way. (The method by which the effect is obtained is called *abreaction*.) The theoretical foundation of those concepts is the psychoanalytic view of memory as an autonomous, innate quality of the mental apparatus whose basic contents become drawn into conflict in the early stages of the psychosexual development by the efforts of the immature ego to resolve its tensions. Deferred gratification during the conflict induces a hallucinatory fulfillment of a wish resulting from the hypercathexis of the memory of a direct gratification. Failure to achieve gratification favors the formation of new memory traces which are more concrete and realistic and contribute to the infant differentiation between the self and the nonself and consequently, to the development of the sense of reality. The short period of autonomy in retaining memory traces is followed by a period in which conflict arises and thus, the early forgetting. Memory is always implicated in whatever ego functions are involved in conflict. The resolution of a defense can be inferred clinically by the emergence of a repressed memory.[215]

From what has preceded, one can understand why the greatest forgetting occurs during infancy. Psychoanalytic interpretation gives it the significance of a defense mechanism of the ego against the castration anxiety of the Oedipal period which initiates this whole phase, from the fourth to the eighth year to the latency period of the psychosexual development.

The shifting from symbols of one developmental stage to another one in an attempt to get away from threatening impulses seems to be the mode in which memory is used as a mental defense mechanism, also according to Jaffe's interpretation. This author[208] gives as an example the case of a man who could not think of the name of a car, a Mustang specifically, and thinks of a Falcon or a Thunderbird to facilitate the recall of that name. Through analytical procedure, it became clear that the patient blocked the recall mechanism of the name "Mustang" because horses represented threatening aggressive impulses originally connected with the anal stage. Shifting from the name of a horse to the names of birds expressed the patient's effort to utilize more comforting associations of the oral nursing experience of his early life. The name "Mustang" was recalled as soon as the analytic working through brought to free expression those painful emotions. Conversely, remembering the name "Mustang" helped indeed to ward off other threatening feelings coming this time from the oral phase of psychosexual development which previously helped in recalling the expressed Mustang name.

Catharsis has become particularly effective in treating *hysterical neurosis,* in which repression works consistently through isolation of a system of learned behavior or memories and its functional disassociation from other systems. Hysterical individuals, in fact, appear endowed of an exceptional power of inhibition and a strong capacity of allocating memory traces to other positions of the ego, as in the self-representation by a process of identification. They also show an innate inclination, with a particular mode of learning, to structure experience into self-contained schemata.[26] The fugue state and the disassociation or loss of personal identity and possible development of multiple personalities are not only further expressions of the psychopathological structure of subjects affected by hysterical neurosis, but are also particularly informative in furnishing immediate evidence of the influence of intense emotional reactions on the organization of experience in the form of memory.[214, 336] As a matter of fact, an emotional stress of a different nature may precipitate the loss of personal identity or fugue states, followed by loss of personal identity, and subsequently, followed by total forgetting for the period over which the dissociative syndrome prevailed.

Other psychoneuroses, such phobic, obsessive-compulsive, anxiety, and depressive neurosis do not share with hysterical neurosis the character of learning and memory impairment, except for the inability to cope with situations in order to overcome a disabling symptom.[392c] Psychotic and, to a lesser extent, nonpsychotic depressions, conversely, are characterized by impaired learning and distorted memory. In *schizophrenia,* deficient registration and recall due to susceptibility to distraction and poor attention, not to mention the primary disorder of thought process with loosening of associations and delusional material, may impair both learning and memory functions. In paranoid schizophrenia, perceptual misconstruction and distortion in thinking and recall mechanisms determined by motivational factors alter the content of memories to the extent that, for example, an attack by the patient is recalled as an attack to the patient. Learning, too, becomes in general remarkably impaired in paranoid schizophrenics because of the conflict between the recently acquired information and that rigidly preconceived. Another characteristic of the recall in paranoid schizophrenics is the richness in detail, related in general to delusional structures, and its stability against any diminution of content *(hypermnesia of schizophrenics).* *

This mode of remembering is in service of defense and conflict which represents a reinstinctualization of nonaggressive and libidinal energies.[214] It sharply contrasts the remembering of the aged and of the infirm in which the excessive functioning of recall, or as it has been said,[215] the libidinization of remembering, is a substitute for a lack of pleasure in current daily living. A basic requirement for remembering, in fact, is the absence of conflict. The *forgetting of the aged,* at least that of the early

---

*Hypermnesia is also termed the vivid or abnormally detailed recollection of events which occurs after the administration of certain drugs or, as commonly believed, after an extremely intense emotional interference, such as the fear of death or the anxiety of survival.

stages of senility when there is no clinical evidence of organic impairment of the brain functioning, may express intrapsychic conflict associated generally with waning powers and the lengthening shadow of death. The process of *forgetting, occurring during the mourning reaction,* may also result from a conflict focused on the disassociation from the love object of the memories originally bound to it. The end result, more evident as stronger is the process of memory decathecting, is forgetting through identification with the mourner's self, a process similar to that occurring in neurotics, especially hystericals.

Regarding the relationships between repression and learning and memory impairment, both as valuable constituents of normal function and as manifestations of psychopathology, an interesting phenomenon observed in amnesic patients suffering from war neurosis deserves brief discussion. *Intravenous administration of barbiturates* has been proved valuable in allowing patients to *recall memories* partially repressed so that they found an outlet in symptom formation. (Pentothal sodium is also known in this respect as "the drug of truth.") The interpretation of this effect as a disinhibition of traumatic experiences has been debated by some authors,[422] but it is a fact that drugs such as minor tranquilizers are able to increase conditioned suppression in rats by facilitating the retrieval of the shock memory.[382] Stein and Berger[382] have recently shown a paradoxical fear-increasing effect of benzodiazepine tranquilizers or of amobarbital (conditioned suppression of feeding as an index of fear) and have interpreted this by considering that those drugs may facilitate the retrieval of painful memories. The drug-induced increase in conditioned fear varied directly with the intensity of the shock used in fear conditioning. The same drugs have no such effect in unshocked controls or in rats made forgetful by electroconvulsive shock given immediately after the fear conditioning.

These data are in line with the classical clinical observations that the intravenous administration of barbiturates facilitates the remembering of partially forgotten information. The retrieval of painful experience in form of memory, therefore, may be inhibited or repressed in animals as well as in man. One of the implications of the data reported above is that the act of recall has some of the properties of the behavioral acts of operant responses[382] in the sense that recalling memories may be facilitated by reward and inhibited by punishment, as are behavior responses. To quote Stein and Berger: "This idea suggests a simple mechanism for the repression of painful memories. As the memory of a painful experience is aroused, the incipient memory activates an inhibitory or punishment process which shifts off the act of retrieval. Tranquilizers interrupt the negative feedback process by blocking the punishment system[3, 50] and thus release the painful memory from repression. Facilitated recall of painful memories may be accomplished by a complementary process. In this case the incipient, positive memory activates the reward mechanism, which facilitates the act of retrieval."

Derangements of learning and memory caused and sustained by brain damage constitute another group in addition to that of psychogenic impairment of those functions, which were described above and in which the part played by emotional factors is prominent. The term "amnesia" refers to the total unavailability of memories and the complete failure in learning.[421] The term "paramnesia" refers to the disturbance of memory function in which the recollection of memories is partially correct but in general, misplaced and jumbled (this false recollection is also called *pseudoreminiscence*), also because of the failure to recognize an illusory memory as such. That recollection may be also entirely overwhelmed by a compulsive tendency to invent stories and make false statements (false recollections especially common in testimony); this is also known as *pseudologia fantastica*. Paramnesias also include *errors in reference*. These make a new experience appear familiar as a replica of an earlier one. The perceptual type involving vision and known as *déjà vu phenomenon* is particularly common as a part of the memory disorder occurring in temporal lobe seizures. The opposite phenomena of *jamais vu* and *jamais entendu*, the consequent common, innocent plagiarism of adults, the appropriation of other persons' actions (common in senility and known as *cryptomnesia*), or the more rare, reverse misattribution called *projection* are also interpreted as errors in reference. Perhaps Janet's interpretation[209] of *déjà vu* as a perception disturbance rather than as a true memory derangement, i.e. a negation of the present nature of an event rather than an affirmation of its pastness, is the most correct one. As a matter of fact, those phenomena occur more often after an epileptic discharge which interrupts the normal electrical activity of the brain, thus interrupting the perceptual process, and therefore, splitting it into the present as well as into a past experience. Freud's analytical interpretation of the feelings of familiarity or unfamiliarity with a new experience[134a-c] recognizes a cause-effect relationship between them and an association unknown to the individual. Ferenczy[123] believes that even a forgotten dream may represent that association.

The *associative pseudoreminiscence* described by Kraepelin[239] in 1887 is well represented by the case of a person who falsely recollects having met someone in some place or having done something with him when seeing or hearing about a person. In general, these types of *memory illusions* originating from factual source are not stable in the sense that they may vary a great deal in contrast to false recollections based on dreams or hallucinations. They may stabilize, however. *Identifying pseudoreminiscence* was called by Kraepelin[239] the temporal reference type of paramnesia in which events as they happen are experienced as if they had been foretold in a dream as a warning and therefore been known in detail before their occurrence (*pseudopresentiments*).

Another interesting paramnesic phenomenon is *confabulation*, which occurs most often in Korsakoff's psychosis. It represents a particular type of pseudoreminiscence as well as a deliberate and imaginative fabrication. While *mytomania* more specifically refers to the invention of fantastic tales, confabulation is the verbal supply of mnemonic material, in general autobiographic in nature, in the unconscious attempt to fill the gaps of the patient's personal memories. The tendency to confabulate decreases as the disorientation recedes, but this is not an absolute fact, and a notable part in making exception to this rule is played by the critical attitude and the insight into the memory disturbance.

While confabulation is always present in the early state of the amnesic syndrome of different natures, it may recede completely in the late stage of the memory disturbance, being gradually replaced by readiness to admit ignorance.

Organic amnesias are classified according to different criteria. The etiologic criterion divides amnesia into amnesia because of trauma, surgical ablations of the cortical tissue of temporal or frontal lobes, electroshock, and pathological conditions of the cerebral tissue. The latter includes such conditions as epileptic foci, tumors in the reticulolimbic system, infections involving the region of the third ventricle, prolonged anoxia with brain damage, cerebrovascular accidents, metabolic and toxic conditions, including alcoholic toxemia and related nutritional deficiency, and degenerative processes, such as those occurring during senescence and presenile and senile brain disease. The chronologic criterion, in the sense of the duration of the memory disturbance, by which an amnesia may be transient or definitive, is often etiologic, too. As a matter of fact, senile amnesia, independent of degeneration of the cerebral cortex, is chronic and irreversible, while some forms of transient amnesias, such as the traumatic and the epileptic amnesias as well as those due to alcoholism, vitamin B deficiency, and some toxemias, may become irreversible as a consequence of permanent brain damage.

A classification which takes into account *how* the memory derangement takes place, in terms of the phase or process of the memory function, or the function which is most impaired, is that which distinguishes *retrograde* and *retroactive amnesias* from *anterograde amnesias*. This criterion is also valuable in giving satisfactory explanation of most of the clinical signs and symptoms of the memory dysfunction as well as of the impairment of learning. If, in the true *primary mental deficiency*, the limited capacity for learning expresses an impaired mechanism of processing and organizing information, the process of retention not being necessarily involved (the memory prodigies, that were feebleminded, have been described on page 7) in the *secondary type of mental deficiency* (represented by the learning deficit of individuals affected by an amnesic syndrome), the trouble, also indicated as anterograde amnesia, consists of an impairment of the registration, retention, or both. A patient's incapacity for recalling past events, in fact, is never so severe as to account for his inability to remember practically nothing of what he perceives. In addition, the testing by recognition rather than by recall of reproduction hardly relieves a patient's learning deficit.

The difficulty or gap in recalling events preceding a patient's illness (trauma, epilepsy, Korsakoff's psychosis, and other causes of brain damage) is also known as *retrograde amnesia*. *Retroactive amnesia* is that which spans a shorter time period than retrograde, for example, for seconds, minutes, or hours, as in the epileptic amnesia, rather than years or the entire life as it occurs more commonly in other organic amnesias. In epilepsy the derangement of memory function involves not only the events occurring in the state of unconsciousness and those preceding it, but also the events following the fit (*postictal anterograde amnesia*). While the *retroactive amnesia* is variable and usually shrinks with time, the *postseizure anterograde amnesia* is more stable and of short duration, except in the case of numerous epileptic fits following each other in a short period of time. An interesting finding concerning learning and memory functions in epilepsy is that while patients are amnesic about the events occurring during the seizure, they can learn while in the twilight state.

In *posttraumatic amnesia* the *anterograde component* because of failure in registration and retention (which makes boxers and football players, who suffered head concussions and continue their sport activity, recall nothing they did during that time), is usually more extended than the retroactive component which is due to failure in consolidation, retention, and recall. The latter, however, takes a shorter time than the former to recover. This occurs gradually by the disorganized appearance of "islands of memories," the older ones being the first to return (according to Ribot's first law of regression; see page 25) and those preceding the accident of just a few minutes, still remaining lost.

The study of retrograde amnesia which is due to trauma has given the chance to Kamin to propose the term *intermediate memory* to indicate a phase of memory in between the short-term memory and the long-term memory. Kamin[218] noted that a typical retrograde amnesia can be detected in subjects who had suffered from head trauma just a few minutes before, but this cannot be duplicated if about thirty minutes elapsed between the trauma and the testing of memory function. The still efficient memory in the lapse of time between the few minutes and the thirty minutes after the trauma suggests that the memory trace would have been stored in a different form, if one assumes that a long-term memory defect implies disruption of the short-term memory. Kamin has also noted that rats taught to avoid punishment in a shuttle-box remember correctly and consistently the learned experience from one minute up to two days after training but show a typical dip in performance between three and six hours—the so-called Kamin effect—in relationship to an inequal rate of growth and decay of the intermediate and long-term memory.

Amnesia due to electroshock is similar to that which is due to epilepsy as far as the recollection of events occurring during the shock is concerned. The simultaneous firing of neuronal units because of electric current is analogous to the synchronization of neuronal function during the epileptic seizure. The *retroactive component* which is due to impairment of retention and recall is of brief duration (a few seconds, and it tends to decrease with ultrabrief stimuli)[84] but may extend back for hours[83a] or one week.[82] No evidence of amnesia, however, has been noted one month after the shock.[83b] The *anterograde component* is more important than the retroactive because of its effects on new learning.

In the *amnesic syndrome due to other causes,* such as Korsakoff's psychosis,[342] brain tumors or infections, anoxia, toxemia, etc., the initial phase is characterized by a confusional state so severe that patients appear totally out of touch with the environment, apathetic or agitated, often talking incoherently or producing delusional thoughts, or even filling the gaps of recent and past memories by confabulation. The disorientation of this confusional state is total and remains such even in the subacute phase of the illness when the patient is capable of perception in the environment and of engaging in normal conversation, but still shows poor grasping of the situation in which he is placed. It has been said[392c] that the world of an amnesic patient is without continuity since time has come to stop for him because of his severe *retrograde amnesia*.

The *anterograde component* of the amnesic syndrome is also important clinically since the severity of the registration disturbance makes the retention of new information extremely difficult or even impossible, with a consequent significant learning deficit especially concerning personal experiences. Interesting is the fact that, while the retention impairment appears usually severe (a name and address may be lost within a few minutes after their presentation), the immediate recall, such as tested by the standard digit span, is usually within normal limits. The less immediate recall, however, is again poor, especially if the patient at some point becomes distracted from the task, or interference created by the registration process enters the picture.

The *retrograde component* of the amnesic syndrome is only occasionally total, i.e. involves the entire life of the patient, more often involving a remarkable amount of personal as well as impersonal experiences and events. "Islands of memories" are recollected in disordered chronological order, thus creating contradictions of which the patient is not aware, but which still contribute to confabulation to fill in the memory gaps. Despite the severity of the retrograde and anterograde components, patients affected by the amnesic syndrome of different organic natures retain the command of well-practiced skills, such as spoken and written language and the common rules of socialization. However, the amnesic patients gradually show lack of interest, initiative, and spontaneity and appear carefree first and totally detached later on, being progressively less capable of sustaining any affective response as well as any critical attitude. All the phases of memory function being impaired, they also appear unable to recognize things, issues, and events and to compare and utilize the contextual clues necessary in recognition and recall to avoid or correct errors. Because of the presence of those several intellectual, emotional, and behavorial signs and symptoms in patients affected by severe and irreversible memory function impairments, the term amnesic syndrome is preferred to that of organic amnesia.

Memory derangement because of *physiological ageing (or senescence)*, which is also indicated as "benign forgetfulness of the old age,"[240] is characterized essentially by impairment of the registration phase which overrules that of recognition and recall phases. It appears clinically evident at about the seventh decade of life, but it can manifest itself earlier or later in life as an expression of unexpected concausal factors as well as of expected factors leading to decomposition and disorganization of the biological matter, both primary or secondary to arteriosclerotic impairment of the circulation of the cerebral cortex. Aged people show a reduced capacity to process and retain new information and to recall at will at least recent memories. There is no disorientation, and memories of personal experiences as well as of recent events are in general preserved. Reduced motivation, decreased state of arousal—or its increase with inherent interference of the autonomic system functioning—are cofactors. Interference, inherent not only to the process of coding new information, but also to that of recalling already well-stored memory traces, is an important source of deterioration of memory function in old age. The slowed rate at which mnemonic data are ordered and transformed in code systems also contributes a great deal. The result is a fragmented filing and an incomplete and inefficient scanning out of information, temporary misplacement of memories, tendency toward perseverance, and stereotyped behavior.

With advancing age the process and the syndrome of organic amnesia gradually change into *presenile* and later on into true *senile dementia,* the impairment of reasoning ability becoming prominent. The impairment of learning and memory functions, however, remains dominant and becomes more severe with time. It is termed *presbyophrenia* so it may be better distinguished from the *senile psychoses,* in which the memory deficit is more remarkable and impressive.[10] Senile dementia reflects an impairment of total mental functioning, but the associated learning and memory derangement is also so severe that it has also been called *malignant forgetfulness of the elderly*[240] in contrast to the benign form discussed above. In the degenerative and atrophic processes of the cerebral cortex clinically known as Alzheimer's disease and Pick's disease, the command of even the well-established skills, such as those of eating, dressing, and cleaning, is lost. In learning and memory defects of senility, dysphasias and apraxias are often associated with a defect in processing new information and recalling proper names and events in the correct sequence as well as familiar places in the true spatial relationship. Another characteristic of senile amnesic patients is that they are talkative and monotonous in their stereotyped repetition of a story, which may or may not have any relationship with the patient's background or recent events.

The amnesia following temporal or frontal lobe surgery or temporal lobe pathology is also discussed on pages 56-59. The retrograde amnesia which may be associated with it is usually moderate as far as its temporal span is concerned in contrast to that associated with Korsakoff's syndrome.

Another interesting type of amnesia which is transient like the amnesia associated with epilepsy or some of the less severe and reversible traumatic amnesias, that due to electroshock treatment included, is the so-called *transient global amnesic syndrome,* which has recently been described as a sudden loss to lay down durable memories lasting from about two to eight hours.[125, 293, 368] The term syndrome is justified by the fact that the subjects affected by this memory disorder (in general individuals 50-60 years old) are usually anxious, hypertensive, and disoriented in time. Initially considered as psychogenic in nature, it has been interpreted more recently as resulting from an altered anastomotic circulation between the basilar and the internal carotid territory of supply and consequent hypoxia of the hippocampus and of the region of the cerebral cortex supplied by the posterior choroidal arteries.

A deficit of memory function limited to the immediate memory has been described recently by Melges *et al.*[279a] in a study of the effects of marihuana on temporal disintegration, i.e. a state which causes "difficulty in retaining, coordinating, and serially indexing those memories, perceptions, and expectations that are relevant to the goal he [the individual] is pursuing." High oral doses of tetrahydrocannabinol extracted from marihuana significantly impaired the serial coordination of cognitive operations during a task which required sequential adjustments in reaching a goal due to the reversible impairment of short-term memory. Because of the defect of immediate memory, the components of speech become poorly coordinated over time, words and phrases are no longer hierarchically ordered in a goal-directed fashion, speech pattern becomes disorganized, and looseness of thought association becomes evident. Speech alteration during marihuana intoxication is interpreted by the authors[279a] as resulting from the temporal incoordination of recent memories with intentions.

INFLUENCE OF HEREDITY AND ENVIRONMENT ON LEARNING AND MEMORY

Genetic Factors

There is no doubt that learning and memory are influenced by environmental factors even though the knowledge of the limits of their effects is rather little. However, independent of the most direct influence of heredity on behavior, which is particularly emphasized by geneticists and pathologists, what is inborn in a human subject or animal has an important part in adaptive behavior (aptitude to respond to a conditioned stimulus, to learn, to remember). Genetic factors influence not only the instincts (which are fixed patterns of behavior reactions) and the more or less organized forms of behavior in animals (such as aggression, sexual drive, finding or building a place to live, etc.), but also any type of motivational or emotional behavior and any response of the individual to the environment. It also controls the ability of higher forms of being to benefit from experience and culture.

Animal experimentation on the influence of inborn and acquired factors on behavior has aided a great deal over the past few decades in the understanding of the determinants and the mechanisms of behavior. One of the early and basic investigations, which aimed to establish whether a given behavioral pattern is genetically transmitted, was that by Tryon[407] about thirty-five years ago. The results of this study based on rigorous control of breeding and environmental factors (for example, by selecting among the offspring those rats with a high or low performance in a standardized maze and then by breeding their offspring) was that bright rats are produced by bright parents, and dull rats, by dull parents.

Several authors have devoted themselves to behavioral genetics since Tryon's first study in which animals bred selectively from genetically homogeneous strains were used.[75, 132, 168, 188, 351, 356, 401] The method to study adaptive behavior was based on giving a reward as a motivational factor. But avoidance conditioning, originally utilized by a minority of investigators,[75, 351, 354] has gained general preference.[44] It consists of recording a conditioned avoidance response when the mouse in a double compartment avoids the shock by running into the other compartment within five seconds after the turning on of a light (conditioned stimulus). The unconditioned stimulus is represented by a continuous electric shock administered through the grid floor of the cage. The mouse's shuttling into the adjacent compartment after the onset of the shock represents the unconditioned escape response. The laboratory animal's submission to this avoidance conditioning fundamentally duplicates a sort of hereditary behavior. Acting out an escape reaction is analogous to the condition of staying alert or escaping from a wild animal in order to survive. The double compartment grill box technique (avoidance as motivation) has been considered preferable to that which uses reward as motivation in studying operant behavior. In addition, the avoidance conditioning requires numerous trials, and the inherent complexity of the task permits adequate study of different phases of the learning mechanism.

By using this experimental approach for the study of the genetic aspects of learning and memory Bovet et al.[44] have succeeded in establishing a significant variability of responses in common non-inbred strains of mice in both different levels of performance by each subject and in different sessions (sharp decrement between consecutive sessions because of freezing behavior,* even though the emotional response is minimal in mice). As a consequence of this finding, the authors relied upon selective breeding of one strain of mice in order to obtain a line of mice with high performance in the shuttle-box (selective breeding continued until the third generation and produced a population of mice with an 85 per cent level of performance in the avoidance conditioning) and to reduce progressively the individual variability. (Selective breeding decreased the fiducial limit of the mean from 23% to 4% in the third generation.)

In further experiments the comparison of performance in avoidance learning between different strains of selected breeds has shown that the type of learning is genetically determined. This seems particularly true in view of the quantitative difference in performance among different strains of mice and in view of the homogeneity of performance in animals of the same strain, which in turn contrasts to the heterogeneity of performance of randomly bred mice.

The ability of performance in getting through a maze also appears to be genetically determined since some strains of mice perform better; others, rather poorly. Those whose ability, as judged by performance in a maze, is better also show higher learning ability in a shuttle-box avoidance response.

Differences in the performance of learning tasks among strains of inbred mice appear to be qualitative rather than quantitative. Two dependent, different mechanisms of retention seem to be involved in the learning process of different strains. The shape of the acquisition curve is different in various strains of mice; some mice prefer long interrupted training sessions (massed practice); others, a series of short sessions (distributed practice). The problem is to establish the optimal length of the break in order to take advantage of the practice. In massed or distributed practice, when the length of the interval between trials was in-

---

Freezing behavior is a type of emotional behavior characterized essentially by immobility in presence of danger associated with experimental animal neurosis.

creased, or when the variations of the performance during each session and during the interval between consecutive sessions was studied, it appeared that behavioral patterns differ markedly. This fact has been also confirmed by experiments on the effects of fatigue and rest on an avoidance response in men subjected to prolonged avoidance sessions. By comparing the recovery of the performance at the end of a prolonged session in two different strains of mice, the different behavioral response has been again demonstrated. Another interesting finding was the different performance after various rest intervals at the end of a two thousand-trial session. The overall impression was that different mechanisms of memory consolidation are active in various strains of mice after the rest periods, and that the technique used (only in a particular avoidance task) did not appear to interfere with the results obtained.

These data support the concept that genetic factors control both the speed of the conditioning process and the nature of the inherent mechanism of memory storage. Perhaps distributed practice is better than massed practice. In other words, learning is better achieved when practice periods are spaced. During rest, in fact, the "inhibitory" elements, which may build up during the learning process and which are detrimental to performance, would disappear, or possibly an active process of memory consolidation would take place, a process by which the early phase of memory (short-term memory) based on an electrophysiological mechanism (See Chapter III.) may go through an autonomous decay or may be modified by further learning and interference. In the meantime, processes such as preservation, organization, or integration would act on a molecular basis, resulting in the establishment of a long-lasting memory trace. The two-stage concept of memory storage, which will be discussed in detail in Chapters III and IV, gets further support, therefore, from the studies on behavorial genetics, which point to clear discrepancies of the learning curves of different strains of inbred mice. One strain would show, for example, a rather poor mechanism of consolidation of the memory trace and a satisfactory short-term memory, and vice versa.

Environmental Factors Influencing Learning and Memory

The morphological and biochemical study of brain tissue of laboratory animals at different times (hours, weeks, months, years) of exposure to a sensory-impoverished environment has shown that the cerebral cortex is 5 per cent thinner than that of controls. Conversely, the cortex of animals exposed to a sensory-enriched environment contains larger neurons and larger and more numerous glial cells as well as higher acetylcholinesterase and cholinesterase activity, greater protein concentration, and better blood supply than the controls.[32, 33, 99, 242, 347, 348] So-called colony-animals were put in cages, two to three per cage, the enriched animals allowed to leave the cages frequently. The impoverished animals, conversely, were kept singly, without toys, in cages located in a dark environment and were handled only once a week for weighing.

The environmental impoverishment seems to cause the most impressive changes in the morphological and biochemical makeup of brain tissue. Even though any relationship between cerebral changes and behavioral changes have not been proved yet in a strictly scientific way, it appears that animals which grew up in a sensory-enriched environment, especially those of the younger age group, show a better problem solving ability, such as, for example, getting through a maze.

Other experiments[144c] have shown that the ability of the optic nerve impulses to activate the appropriate neurons in the visual cortex becomes defective in the eye of kittens which have been maintained blindfolded for three weeks. Analogously, chimpanzees shielded from patterned visual experiences for a period of weeks are unable to discriminate visually and are functionally blind. It has been also found that the inhibition of one cerebral hemisphere by KCl during learning limits the memory trace to the opposite hemisphere in mammals. As a matter of fact, the inactivation of the latter causes the loss of the learned response.

By extrapolating the results of the studies on animals reported above into the field of human behavior, it seems possible to establish analogies concerning the validity of the concept that the abilities of man can be enhanced by appropriate designed experience.

(Learning, in fact, is a modification of behavior in response to experience.) It has been noted that a delay up to two years in starting to walk occurs in orphans raised with adequate physical care, but insufficient social attention. When these children (and normal subjects, too) are brought into an improved environment, their I.Q. increases up to twenty points or more. On the basis of that assumption and those facts, and taking into account the parallelism between the increase of cerebral volume in man and the development of new tools, the so-called computer aided learning has been envisaged,[144d] with the aim to make education a science rather than only an art. (In fact, education attempts to pattern the experience received.) Computers could help in building up better brains because they can tailor experience to the individual child and give to the privileged or underprivileged youngsters the equivalent of an understanding, informed, and infinitely patient tutor.[144d] This view seems to be shared by other investigators. [54, 74, 148, 406]

Further support to the influence of environmental factors on learning and memory has been given by those experiments which have investigated the effects of weaning on behavior. Ressler,[338] for example, has shown that fastening affects the behavior of mice reared by alien foster mothers or the behavior resembles that of an alien strain. Denenberg and Karas[92] have demonstrated that the maternal environment affects emotional reactions of offspring. Bovet-Nitti *et al.*[44] have found that while some emotional components of behavior are strongly affected, the usual patterns of avoidance behavior of mice in a shuttle-box is not by cross-fostering of two inbred strains of mice. By measuring avoidance and "freezing behavior," the authors found that the modification of the preweaning environment affects the emotional behavior whereas variations of learning patterns are due to the concomitant appearance of "freezing behavior." The emotional, not the adaptive, behavior seems to be influenced by the modification of the environment.

Other studies have drawn attention to the effects of free environmental experience and of early visual and motor experience as determinants of a rat's ability to solve problems in a maze.[130]

Different experimental stimuli such as visual, acoustical, and thermic as well as momentary handling of the animal could facilitate or inhibit the ability to condition and discriminate.[93, 231, 253, 273c, 370] Finally, it has been demonstrated that several environmental factors, such as light, diet, and olfactory stimuli, are able to influence the sexual behavior and the sexual equilibrium of male and female mice.[53, 374]

Nutritional Factors Influencing Learning and Memory

Malnutrition interferes with learning and memory functions during the growth of an individual, animal or human, both in the fetal or prenatal life and in the early postnatal or neonatal life.[112, 360, 424] Malnutrition after birth is only partially responsible for impairment of those functions as well as of the inherent behavioral deviations and of the respective physical changes. Animal studies have shown that prenatal nutritional deprivation reduces cellular growth of the brain to the point that irreversible damage occurs, even though strong corrective efforts are made subsequently.[424] This is also true for any other organ, but the brain seems to be most sensitive; it is certainly a unique organ which, if damaged, may affect man's ability to improve his life and that of other men with whom he is in social contact. As a matter of fact, 80 per cent of the adult brain size is attained at normal weaning time in rats and pigs and within the first three years of life in man, while at the same developmental stage body weight is only 20 per cent of that in adult age. The earlier in life malnutrition occurs, the more profound and permanent is the impairment of the ability to learn and memorize. The degree of malnutrition, however, is still unknown.

Growth, either in intrauterine or in postnatal life, may be considered in terms of increase in size or weight of the body as a whole or of individual organs. The rate of net protein synthesis expresses the rate of growth. Growth stops when the equilibrium between protein synthesis and protein degradation is attained. Since protein synthesis appears to be a linear process in prenatal and postnatal life, growth may be considered as a homogeneous process. However, if growth is considered in cellular terms, i.e.

as an increase in number or size of the cells or both, then growth appears to be a nonhomogeneous process because a phase in which an organ grows by increase in cell number is followed by a phase in which the same organ continues to grow by increase in cell size.

It is particularly in the phase in which an organ grows by increase in cell number that malnutrition may cause irreversible damage by leaving a permanent deficit in cell number. Since the concentration of DNA fixed in the diploid nucleus of the cells of a given species (6.2 picograms in the rat and 6.0 in man) is stable, measurement of DNA makes possible the determination of the total number of the cells of a given organ at a given time. Cell size may be calculated by dividing the weight or protein content by the number of the cells. The study of the cell growth, initiated in 1962 by the Canadians Enesco and Leblond (quoted in Winick[424]), has also shown that there is a first phase of this process which is due primarily to rapid cell proliferation but with a proportional increase in organ weight or protein content and that a second phase, in which cell proliferation continues but at a slower rate than cell enlargement, as well as a third phase follow, during which growth is due entirely to increase in cell size.

Further studies in the past decade have also shown that the cell growth sequence in laboratory animals, such as rodents, applies equally to man, regarding the cell growth sequence both in fetal and neonatal life.[424] Before birth, growth proceeds almost entirely by cell division (progressive increase in DNA content for the whole animal and of individual organs from the 10th day after conception—when observation began—for varying times after birth), while cell size remains constant (cell weight and protein increase proportionately). With further growth the rate of DNA synthesis slows down in all organs, and it stops in the brain by the twentieth postnatal day, i.e. earlier than in lungs, heart, and muscle (44th postnatal day for the latter two organs). This indicates that cell growth proceeds by cell enlargement alone when the organ has attained maximum weight or protein content, which occurs some time after DNA synthesis has stopped.

Parallel to the decrease of DNA synthesis, protein concentration continues to increase, thus indicating that the increase in cell enlargement is due to decreased cell division rather than to increased rate of protein accumulation.

Variations in growth patterns were also observed within individual regions of the rat brain in the early postnatal period. Different regions of the rat brain, in fact, reach the final number of cells (as expressed by DNA synthesis value) at different times. DNA synthesis stops sooner in the cerebral cortex (14th day) than in the cerebellum (17th day) and brain stem (21st day). In the cerebellum it also proceeds faster. The experiments carried out on young rats undernourished since birth have shown that all areas of the nervous system where cells are dividing suffer from undernutrition because of the slowing down or arrest of cell division. The cerebellum, whose cells divide more rapidly than cortical neurons and neurons of the brain stem, is affected first by malnutrition. In the cerebral cortex only glial cells appear reduced in number since rat neurons do not divide after birth. In the human brain, however, DNA synthesis is thought to be coterminous in the cerebral cortex and the cerebellum (8th month) and to occur sooner than in the brain stem (12th month). By about the 8th month the total number of brain cells is attained. Of all organs, only the placenta terminates its cell division before the brain.

The important implication of these data is that malnutrition may interfere with growth differently according to the developmental phases, both in the prenatal and neonatal periods. The effects of malnutrition are less severe and reversible if they interfere with growth during the phase of cell enlargement, more severe and irreversible if they interfere with growth during the phase of cell proliferation. As far as the effects of malnutrition on the human brain are concerned, the data are still incomplete with respect to those inherent to animal experimentation. But those available indicate that time is also an essential factor in determining the effects of malnutrition on the human brain. If in early life severe malnutrition occurs, brain growth is affected; brain circumference and weight do not reach average values, and protein and nucleic acid concentration as well as DNA polymerase activity are low.[424] The first year of life would be the most crucial regarding the effects of malnutrition on brain development by assuming that the cellular response to malnutrition in the human brain duplicates that of the rat brain.

Clinical observations of infants who died of malnutrition in the first year of life have shown that they were below the third percentile for height and weight and showed the signs of infantile marasma as well as the anatomical and biochemical changes in the brain mentioned above. It has also been shown that a child of low birth weight who is subsequently malnourished may be left with a 60 per cent deficit in brain cell number. The 45 per cent plus difference of this value with respect to that (15%) of a child of normal weight and stature at birth who becomes undernourished subsequently is suggestive of a greater brain vulnerability to a postnatal insult if the prenatal malnutrition had already displayed its effects. Animal investigation has also shown that if dietary deprivation involves more protein than carbohydrates, permanent retardation in developing learning behavior and sluggish responses to various environmental stimuli occur; if it involves more carbohydrates than proteins, those behavioral changes take place, but solving ability is generally preserved.[21, 80, 112]*

The most serious effect of malnutrition in humans is that due to protein deficit, but caloric deficit and lack of vitamins are also significant factors. In human pathology, infantile marasma and Kwashiorkor are two different clinical manifestations of malnutri-

---

*Ability to solve a detour problem in young chickens has been found influenced more by the age or degree of development than by the number of training trials.[359] Before the age of four days or after the age of fifteen days no chick has shown ability to learn. When the peak age for learning was studied in relation to different strains of chicken, it was found that the peak age of the New Hampshire strain is lower than that of the Rhode Island strain of chicken. It has been hypothesized that the concentration of the gamma-aminobutyric acid in brain tissue correlates with the onset of the detour learning since both approach maximal values at about the same age. Overtraining, studied throughout some physiological correlates such as heart rate, palmar skin conductance, and galvanic skin response, cause a sort of habituation of these responses. Double overlearning further decreases them, perhaps also in relationship to the reduction of the apprehension during the course of the experiment.[13]

tion. Early weaning and absence of substitution for human milk is the usual cause of infantile marasma.[94] Late weaning (2-3 years) and lack of food supplement with the inherent protein deficiency are responsible for Kwashiorkor.[106] In both cases children respond sluggishly to environmental stimuli and lack interest and motivation.[112] The electroencephalogram appears markedly abnormal in form, frequency, and amplitude.[412] Intellectual functioning appears grossly impaired on psychological testing. During the phase of recovery from the effects of such nutritional disturbance, if it could take place, attention and motivation are the first to improve, followed by the electroencephalographic recording. Intelligence, however, never returns to the preillness values in severe cases of malnutrition.[345] In underdeveloped countries the poor intellectual functioning of children reared in poverty is certainly influenced by psychological and cultural factors. How much altered motivation and altered capacity influence intelligence as a consequence of malnutrition remains to be ascertained. But the results of animal experimentation reported above seem to point unequivocally to the significant role played by nutrition. They also point to malnutrition as the most prominent factor among the multiple socioeconomic factors which may influence intellectual functioning and behavior. It has been estimated that at the present time at least 300 million children are suffering from varying degrees of malnutrition. An interesting aspect of this problem is the cause-effect hypothesized relationship between human malnutrition before birth and the subsequent specific developmental problems. It has been shown that fetal growth does not suffer from any severe maternal starvation during pregnancy; birth weight is moderately affected, but prematurity rate remained unchanged.[424] There is no doubt, however, that the risk of abnormal fetal nutrition and growth is higher in infants whose mothers are malnourished during pregnancy. The quantitative aspect of the malnutrition remains to be ascertained.

An interesting acquisition of recent years (1965-1968) has its roots in a study of the World Health Organization aimed to determine the effects of infection on nutritional status, the effects of malnutrition on resistance to infection, and the qualitative and quantitative effects of the interaction between nutrition and infection. The important finding of this study is that the two factors, malnutrition and infection, interact with each other to the extent that the combined effect is quantitatively greater than that of each factor separately considered and then added to the other. It has been found, for example, that the mortality rate does not necessarily decrease if a population in a rural area is given medication for prevention of infection or supplementary food, or as an alternative, if it is given better sanitation facilities for prevention of disease. On the other hand, it has been ascertained than when infection superimposes its effects on the effects due to malnutrition, a condition such as Kwashiorkor may develop and most of the time lead to death. An infectious disease has more chances to develop in a malnourished individual because of his increased susceptibility to pathogenetic organisms. On the other hand, a malnourished child may survive, even if severely ill, until he gets an infection which, per se, is only rarely lethal in a well-nourished organism.

The important implication of those studies is that action aimed at the simultaneous control of malnutrition and infection is the most appropriate way to fight the poor health of underdeveloped populations. For those communities which are not underdeveloped, better nutrition may be assured by the correction of commercial food products, for example, by the addition of 0.25 lysine, other than needed vitamins and minerals to cereal foods (wheat and its products). As a matter of fact, a significant part of the population gets its nutrition from food, such as grain derivatives (in general less expensive than meat), which provide adequate caloric intake but not enough protein material, especially of the essential amino acids, lysine primarily.

Chapter II

LOCALIZATION OF LEARNING AND MEMORY IN THE BRAIN

The first acquired fact opposing theories, speculations, and hypotheses about the problem of learning and memory localization in the brain was offered in the late twenties by Karl Lashley in the United States. None of the thirty different types of incisions in the rat brain, deep enough to interrupt the neural pathways, appeared to interfere with a given learned performance inherent to the specific pathway interrupted. Only a general lowering of the accuracy of the discrimination was noted: for example, when up to 90 per cent of the primary visual cortex was made dysfunctional by the surgical procedure.[250a] At the conclusion of his studies Lashley envisaged a cerebral localization of behavior so diffusely represented as well as a brain functioning so widespread to reach the point, perhaps excessive, of considering any part of the cerebral cortex as able to carry out almost any function. This concept is also known as *equipotentiality of brain functioning*.

The influence of Lashley's research on the understanding of the general mechanics of the brain has been impressive. Confirmation of that research has been also provided by many clinical studies. It has been shown, for example, that the injury of even large areas of the cerebral cortex as well as brain damage because of trauma, tumors, abscesses, circulatory disturbances, and ageing do not affect necessarily and specifically learning and memory functions.[166a] Infants and very young children represent an exception: they perform poorly if the cerebral cortex is damaged, thus indicating that the cerebral cortex is necessary to acquire the so-called environmental intelligence, i.e. that less predetermined by genetical factors and not as necessary to retain experiential information.

A fundamental achievement in the understanding of the problem of learning and memory localization, as representative of an

55

alternate concept of general brain functioning, is the contribution given by the Canadian neurosurgeon Wilder Penfield[314a-d] in the middle fifties. Penfield and Jaspers[315] first observed that the stimulation of the cortex of the superior or lateral surface of both healthy or diseased temporal lobe with a low-voltage current (during brain surgery in an epileptic patient) elicited the recollection of old, forgotten memories (thoughts, music) and the concomitant revival of the inherent emotions. The effect disappeared on the turning off of the stimulating current. If applied to other regions of the brain the electric stimulation did not elicit any memory recollection. The difference between normal remembering and the type of remembering resulting from stimulation of the temporal lobe is that the latter is more specific and strictly bound to the occasional circumstances of a particular event, rather than more abstract and conceptual.

The function of the temporal lobe, according to Penfield,[314a-d, 317] is interpretive, the response being a "sudden signal of interpretation," i.e. an automatic judgment of the present environment (feeling that the things are familiar, for example). A second type of response would consist, according to the same author, of the activation of the "stream of past experience," the auditory and the visual components being the predominant ones. As a matter of fact, the retrograde amnesia of epilepsy—or more precisely the retroactive amnesia of epilepsy since it usually extends just for a short time (seconds, minutes, or hours) backward with respect to the epileptic seizure—is characterized by a derangement of the sense of familiarity (expressed by a feeling of unreality about one's body or the environment, rather than true loss of identity) and by the so-called *déjà vu* or *jamais vu* phenomena, i.e. the feeling of having or having not seen before someone or something that was (*déjà vu*) or was not (*jamais vu*) encountered for the first time.[315] (See pages 35, 36.)

Penfield's contribution is also valuable as far as the understanding of the temporal lobe role in learning and memory functions is concerned; it was made possible by the study of the effects of temporal lobectomies, most of which occurred in patients affected by temporal lobe epilepsy. Even though the extrapolation of the data inherent to abnormal function into the field of physiological response should be cautious, the data obtained through that method of study appear interesting. Temporal lobectomy usually does not produce permanent memory impairment except if bilateral or, as in the case of unilateral lobectomy, if the opposite temporal lobe is diseased (for example, as resulting from birth injury) or finally, if it is associated with excision of the hippocampus.[316] Unilateral temporal lobectomy usually causes verbal and auditory learning impairment if the resection involves the left dominant hemisphere, and alteration of the visual pattern recognition and of the recognition of melodies (pitch and rhythm excluded) if the resection involves the right nondominant side. A true amnesic syndrome following spontaneous or surgical lesions of temporal lobe develop in a limited number of cases. The subjects retain the memory of special skills and are able to work, but if their attention is turned on something else while they are doing a given task, then they are unable to recall what they did and what plans they had made for the next action. They also show clear-cut difficulty in carrying out instructions and executing the successive steps of an action, and in registering and retaining new learned material, such as not recognizing their own drawings even after a few minutes delay, thus suggesting that the mechanism of recall is anatomically separated from that of recording.[315]*

That the attention of the students of learning and memory was focused initially and essentially on the cerebral cortex in the at-

---

*A recent investigation by Kowe *et al.*[238] has shown that unilateral carotid amobarbital injection provides a useful test for the identification of patients with a high risk of developing significant short-term memory impairment following temporal lobectomy for the removal of an epileptic focus. The first twenty procedures have revealed definitive memory deficit in four patients with 20 per cent incidence, which is reasonably in agreement with that reported in the literature. Since 10-20 per cent of the operated cases are followed by short-term memory loss, the 20 per cent incidence of memory impairment after intracarotid amobarbital injection appears to be significant in spotting the ability to develop memory deficit following lobectomy. After radiographic verification of the position of the needle in the internal carotid artery with 5 cc of Renografin®60, 180 mg of sodium amobarbital in 10 cc of sterile water are injected within three to four seconds. The procedure seems to be complication-free.

tempt to throw more light on the problem of localization of those processes in the brain is understandable by considering that the cortex, especially that of the frontal lobes, has reached the greatest development in man throughout the entire evolution of the species. However, it has been also shown that other areas of the cerebral cortex in man, such as the temporo-parietal area, have developed proportionally even more than the frontal cortex. In addition, it seems that the greater development of the frontal lobes in humans is more closely related to the development of the individual personality traits rather than to the intellectual functioning, learning and memory functions included.

Frontal lobes of man, anyway, are still considered particularly contributing to learning in childhood and responsible for the abstracting ability, evaluation, judgment, and aesthetic sensitivity in adulthood.[19] Systems, implications, and classes are the products of information which become more impaired when frontal lobes are damaged.[144b, 155, 166a, 330e, 381] The results of frontal lobotomies are biased by the fact that the individuals who undertook that type of surgery were severely disturbed prior to it. While there is no evidence of any permanent impairment of learning and memory after frontal lobectomy, poor retention having been occasionally noted for a period of time no longer than two to three years after surgery,[241] it has been shown that learning and memory abilities improve after the operation while the psychotic symptoms and maladaptive behavior subside.[392c] However, patients treated with frontal lobectomy have consistently shown disorientation, learning deficit, distractability, misplacement of memories in time, and tendency to confuse fact with fantasy as well as lack of initiative and drive.

Recently, Pribram *et al.*[330e] have found that lobectomy or partial damage of the frontal cortex in man and monkeys cause memory impairment of events which occurred just a few seconds before the amnesic event. A sort of coding operation resembling that of parsing (or chunking, in Miller's terminology)[283] is grossly impaired in frontal lobe damage. The defect of recall, therefore, seems to be only in part due to the fading of the memory trace. When longer intervals were set during the experiments (which is analogous to the parsing effect), and the experiment itself was adequately structured, the recall improved quickly and significantly.

The same authors[330e] have also found that the frontal cortex is able to control sensory information flowing into the cortical receiving areas, in this respect duplicating the effect of the stimulation of the posterior association cortex, i.e. that to modify the input signals before they reach the specific sensory areas of the cortex. The pathway involved, according to a recent study by Lindsley and Clemente, would be a large tract of fibers running into the medial forebrain bundle which carries inhibitory impulses to the reticular core. (See below.)

In conclusion, the role of the cerebral cortex in learning and memory appears to be that of a refined representation organ accounting for the magnification and multiplication of the sensory input due to the fan-like widespread central distribution of the fibers coming from the lower part of the sensorisensitive system, and allowing the highest degree of organization, correlation, and integration of the incoming information with that previously experienced and permanently stored. But if the cerebral cortex, especially that of the frontal lobes and of the parieto-temporal lobes,* is the main responsible structure of the brain as far as

---

*The temporo-parietal region of the cerebral cortex is encircled by the olfactory, visceral, somesthetic, auditory, and visual areas. It is a part of the *association cortex* that is implicated in those aspects of behavior in which alertness and attention play a major role.[256, 397] It includes an anterior portion, or frontal association cortex, and a posterior portion located within the primary sensory areas.[228] The inferior part of the posterior portion of the association cortex is concerned with visual discrimination; the middle temporal one, with hearing function; the parieto-occipital one, with the sense of touch.[330e] It is in this temporal part of the cerebral cortex, which anatomically and physiologically is closely related to the cortex of the frontal lobes and to that of the specific senses, and to the subcortical structures of the reticulo-limbic system as well, that the combination, correlation, and integration of the input signals representing the memory traces take place. There, the response to stimuli tends to be independent of the specific stimulus parameters, such as quality, intensity, and rate of presentation, at least over certain ranges.[34, 35, 144 b, 366, 399] The study of concept learning in man[158, 180] suggests that shape (whose coding takes place in the visual cortex[192]), color (whose coding takes place at or below the level of the visual thalamus[96]), and number concept (whose coding takes place in the association cortex[399]) may form an ordered series of increasingly complex concepts. The integrative processes

the intellectual functioning in general and learning and memory functions more specifically are concerned, some subcortical structures have been found recently to have a significant part in those functions, especially the structures of the so-called reticulo-limbic system.

Originally known as rhinencephalon (nose-brain), particularly in relationship to its function in animals which is primarily that of olfaction (in man the part played by rhinencephalon in learning and memory is easily understandable taking into account that in animals odors represent the stimuli which elicit sexual activity and aggressive behavior), the limbic system or limbic lobe is so called because it forms a ring or margin (limbus) around the brain stem.[266, 298] Two concentric rings of cortex constitute the limbic lobe. The inner ring, which includes part of the hippocampal formation (hippocampal gyrus and hippocampus), is also known as "archipallium," being philogenetically the most primitive with respect to the outer cortical ring or "mesopallium," which is intermediate anatomically and philogenetically between the "archipallium" and the surrounding "neocortex," responsible for

---

occur throughout the entire brain, and only speech function has a specific localization in one hemisphere, the left one.

According to the results of a recent electrophysiological study in individual neurons of the association cortex of the cat,[399] there are cells which characteristically discharge to a particular numbered stimulus in the series of stimulus presentation, and which, therefore, seem to fulfill the operational requirements necessary to code the concept of number. Five counting cells, which code the numbers 2, 5, 6 (two cells), and 7, have been recognized in the adult cat. Crude estimation suggests that 1 per cent of the cells in the association cortex of the cat which respond to stimuli (i.e. 5 out of 500) are counting cells. That cats can learn to count successive stimuli[268] and that primates can learn to respond to number of objects in simultaneous presentations[185] has been already demonstrated. From the data of Thompson *et al.*[399] one can understand that the association cortex is provided with specific neurons which are responsible for more abstract aspect of perception. The counting cells really appear to behave as though they code the abstract property of number and to be capable therefore of carrying the label of "gnostic cells" given them by Konorski.[236 b] Complex coding results from a predetermined structural organization,[395] and from an innate stimulus characteristic brain model comparison mechanism;[284, 399] but this does not exclude the fact that prior stimulus processing influences the behavior of those cells and that the extent to which the neural coding of the stimuli takes place is based on previous learned experience.[178, 284]

the higher intellectual functions. In addition to the hippocampus the limbic system includes the olfactory bulb, tract, medial and lateral striae, trigone and tubercle, the septum, the amygdaloid nucleus or amygdala, the anterior nucleus of the thalamus, the hypothalamic nuclei, the mammillary body and tract, and the fornix. Within the complex network connecting the olfactory structures of the rhinencephalon, a significant part of the association fibers are those of the medial forebrain bundle which serve as a vital link with the lower brain stem and spinal cord, and the fibers connecting the limbic system with the reticular formation.[263] It is this important anatomo-functional relationship which led to the calling of the reticulo-limbic system and reticular core, respectively, the total associative system and the reticular formation.

The role of the *reticular core* consists essentially of allowing the decoding process of the input signals by the mechanism of convergence discussed above. By convergence of a number of different stimuli unrelated to the information of the input pathway, the neuronal units of reticular core may become activated. The final result is a sort of filtering process of the incoming formation, correlation, and integration with other input signals, and maintenance of a state of vigilance (unconscious awareness, not to be misinterpreted as true conscience or conscious awareness[60a-h]), [35, 108d, 133, 263, 267, 354, 415] through a continuous alerting of the cerebral cortex. The normal functioning of the reticular core also assures the proper usage of the meaning information by the cortical neurons by a sort of selective blockage (through inhibitory fibers directed to the sensory organs) of most of the potential stimuli which are not needed at a given moment; this results in better concentration and attention upon those stimuli which appear actually relevant and significant. As a matter of fact, the cortex becomes unresponsive to coded impulses when the reticular core is inactivated.

The *hypothalamic nuclei,* for their part, play a considerable role in learning and memory processes, because they control both emotional[60a, 186a, b, 263] and adaptive behavior.[118, 181, 302, 303, 411, 425, 428] It has also been shown that the stimulation of the hypothalamic nuclei by a low voltage current reinforces learning and increases motivation, perhaps indirectly through the numerous anatomo-functional connections with the reticulo-limbic system and the cortex of the frontal lobes. It has been said, therefore, that the hypothalamus is the site of "reward" and "punishment" centers.[303] The medial forebrain bundle seems to be the principal neural pathway for the reward system, and the periventricular group of fibers, the main pathway for the punishment system.[381]

As far as the gray structure of the limbic system, known as the *amygdala,* and the mostly gray structure of the temporal lobe, known as the *hippocampus,* are concerned, the part they have in the mechanism of encoding, storing, and retrieving information is still under scrutiny. It has been already mentioned that the bilateral loss of the amygdaloid-hippocampal areas of the temporal lobe causes memory impairment for recent events.[314d, 316, 430] Pribram *et al.*[229, 330b] have shown that bilateral hippocampectomy interferes with learning of a sequence of responses but does not affect simple discrimination. Avis and Carlton[17] have demonstrated recently that the transient suspension of the electrical activity of the hippocampus (by local injection of 12 ml of 25% solution of KCl) as much as twenty-four hours after learning causes retrograde amnesia (detected by measuring the retention of a conditioned suppression [drinking] during the presentation of a tone previously paired with a shock).

Adey *et al.*[2] have shown a significant correlation between the electroencephalographic pattern of the hippocampus in monkeys and cats and high degree of attention. By the time the cat has learned to choose correctly a given arm of a T-maze, the electroencephalographic recording from the hippocampus shows that rhythmicity appears at the moment the animal gets the signal to begin the test and disappears at the approach of its reward. These wave trains persist in the temporal lobe through a high degree of over-training, while other aspects of brain's electrical activity disappear. This could mean that the temporal lobe acts as a pacemaker after the initiation and distribution of the electrical waves throughout other brain regions.[2] The destruction of those areas in the temporal lobe or the interference with their functioning by drugs, such as lysergic acid diethylamide or cyclohexamine, suspends temporarily or permanently the ability to focus attention to the point that recent memory, thus learning, becomes impossible. The relationship between the hippocampal electrical wave pattern and states of attention has been also demonstrated in man.[2]

Other investigators are more inclined to consider significant the contribution of the hippocampus and the amygdala in learning and memory processes only if that contribution is considered together with the part played by the cerebral cortex, the reticular core, and the hypothalamic nuclei.[105, 143, 280a, b, 295] The integrated functioning of all those structures assures the adequate degree of attention, motivation, and reinforcement so that a sort of selecting activity is maintained on all the incoming stimuli. The emotional component of such a filtering process comes primarily from the amygdala among the structures of the reticulo-limbic system. The affective evaluation of the input signals, for example, as pleasant, or unpleasant with the inherent influence on reinforcement and extinction (or habituation), results from the proper functioning of the amygdala. On the other hand, experimental evidence points to a significant part of this structure in controlling primitive instinctual drives, such as fear and aggression.[154] With this respect, however, the diencephalon remains the main structure responsible for the genesis and control of emotions. As a matter of fact, if the connections between the limbic system and the diencephalon are suppressed, no emotions arise.[198] The generally poor therapeutical results of cingulectomy[310, 332]* support the concept that emotional reactions are generated elsewhere. The favorable results obtained by a surgical approach at the level of diencephalo-hypothalamic region, following the therapeutic failure of cingulectomy in severe emotional distress associated with gross paranoid ideation, point to the hypothalamus as the structure of the brain responsible for the genesis of the emotions. The same results of surgery at the hypothalamic level also show how difficult it is to

---

Cingulectomy is a surgical procedure consisting of a large excision of cingular circonvolutions with the resulting suppression of the Papez's circuit, i.e. of that bundle of polysynaptic associative fibers connecting the paramedian frontal cortex and the anterior nucleus of the thalamus with the hippocampus. This circuit has been interpreted by Papez as the anatomic substrate for affective and emotional responses.[309]

reduce the influence of the hypothalamus on emotions by surgical approach. This may indeed increase the emotional symptoms because of the traumatic reaction all around the surgical lesions.[60]

Since Penfield's observation concerning the ability of an electrical stimulation of the temporo-parietal region of the cerebral cortex to elicit the recall of forgotten memories and the reexperience of the inherent emotional reactions, research on brain-behavior relationship has tended to emphasize relatively strict localization of function, i.e. that impairment or prevention of the occurrence of a given behavioral sequence occurs after the removal or the irreversible damage of a particular area of the brain, especially if the removal of the cortical tissue is carried out bilaterally and in a single-stage process.[320] Successive two-stage cortical lesions, conversely, have been shown to have an effect upon retention of a learned discrimination under certain conditions. These data have been recently confirmed by Stein *et al.*[383] by testing acquisition and retention after removal of cortical as well as subcortical structures (the amygdala, for example). The results of this study have shown that acquisition and retention of a variety of learned tasks in rats with one-stage lesions in the frontal cortex, hippocampus, and amygdala were impaired, while in rats with two-stage lesions, they were not.

The importance of those studies is that even though a given structure of the brain may be responsible for a given behavioral response, its absence is not a *conditio sine qua non* for the suppression of that response. The concept of learning and memory delocalization, in other words, appears to overwhelm that memory localization just as Lashley's initial studies pointed out four decades ago. At the present time it is still speculative how recovery of function occurs in mature laboratory animals subjected to lesions in different regions of the brain. Such a functional plasticity of brain functioning has been noted in young laboratory animals[231] in the absence of specific prior learning or rehabilitation training. It is well known that it also occurs in mature organisms. Lashley's original hypothesis about the naturally occurring reorganization process in neural tissue emphasized the overlapping of neuronal fields with the resulting scattered distribution of the memory traces over a large area of the brain. Kennard[226] suggested in 1938 that the function of the removed tissue is taken over by other structures. More recently Luria[261] has suggested that complex adaptive activity is a function of the dynamic integration of the whole central nervous system and that functional systems mediating complex behavior are not fixed in any area of the brain. If those hypotheses do not say too much about the mechanism of the reorganization process in the damaged brain, one fact is sure, i.e. that no regerenation of neural tissue occurs. The unaffected tissue, therefore, must be involved in the recovery of function. In that case the concept of memory localization appears no longer tenable. According to the *redundancy principle,** in fact, neurons tend to increase their activity when other neuronal units are destroyed. In other words, rather than a specific local change of neurons, memory would consist of an alteration of a pattern of many areas of the cerebral cortex following the impression of the information. Contrary to the neuroanatomical approach of the study of learning and memory, the neurophysiological approach does not necessarily imply the structural changes of the brain, but rather a functional reorganization of neurons as single units or networks. Contrary to the hypothesis basic to classical conditioning, the arrangement of neurons seems to be perpendicular to the surface of the cortex rather than parallel to it in form of network.[392]

An interesting trend of investigation of memory delocalization is that which, after the initial experiments by Akelaitis[7] in 1944, has used the so-called split-brain technique first in laboratory animals,[376] then in human beings,[140-142, 146] and has provided evi-

---

*The *redundancy principle,* important in neurophysiology, is also significant for the understanding of the *mechanism of drug addiction.*[384] It may be taken into consideration when, for example, neurons become depressed because of long-standing administration of sedatives or tranquilizers. In this condition, other neuronal units enter into action to compensate for the depressed or suspended activity of the neurons affected by the drug. The consequence is the need for increasing dosage of the drug to curb anxiety, agitation, and even convulsions or coma. In fact, the neurons depressed by the drug regain their usual functioning, and this combines with the functioning of the neurons entered into action during the process of addiction with a resulting overpopulation of neurons more active than is consistent with normal behavior.

dence that, except for verbal messages, information is specularly duplicated in both cerebral hemispheres in the cortex as well as in other regions of the brain.

In Sperry's classical experiment,[376] a monkey learns a task after appropriate arrangements have been made to assure that visual or tactual inputs involve only one cerebral hemisphere. The two hemispheres are then disconnected by sectioning the corpus callosum. The animal is tested for retention of the learned task in the hemisphere opposite to that initially involved in the storage of information. The results have shown that the monkey performs satisfactorily in the noninvolved hemisphere; meanwhile, the memory trace establishes itself within the involved one.

The experiments on split-brain, carried out recently by Gazzaniga[140-142] on a patient who had the cerebral hemispheres surgically disconnected, appear particularly interesting from the standpoint of the functions represented or primarily represented in the left and right hemispheres of the brain. The results have shown that the left hemisphere is mostly associated with figure abilities and functions. Concerning emotion, Gazzaniga has noted that the stimulation of the right hemisphere arouses them. This is also known in the speech (whose center is located in the left hemisphere): there was no verbal understanding of the cause of the emotional reaction. A severed corpus callosum, therefore, while making impossible any significant translation between figural and semantic areas of the information, does not interfere significantly with emotions. Perhaps these are maintained in their bilateral representation by connections located at a level lower than that of the corpus callosum.

More recent investigation by Sechzer[361a] has clarified the contribution of each cerebral hemisphere to learning and memory processes. Split-brain cats were trained in a variety of discriminations and the success or failure of interhemispheric transfer was evaluated with regard to the rate of learning. It has been ascertained that when the interhemispheric transfer fails, learning time is prolonged by about twice the normal time, and retention is also poor. This study indicates that a normal learning curve results from the interhemispheric functional interaction during the process of learning.

Galambos' experiments[137] appear relevant with respect to the concept of memory delocalization. They have shown, in fact, that the conditioned response lost by removing the cerebral cortex may be relearned. More recently the same investigator has demonstrated that severing up to 98 per cent of the optic tract in cats does not seriously impair their ability to perform skillfully on tests requiring differentiation between highly similar figures.[330e] Sperry noted no change in the organization of the input system following the surgical crosshatching of a sensory cortical area of a monkey brain or after putting chips of mica in the crosshatched troughs in an effort to insulate electrically small squares of cortical tissue from others.[330e]

The results of the Pribram and Spinelli[330e] study of visual discrimination in monkeys are similar to those reported above in pointing to the fact that each sensory system has a considerable reserve capacity which is distributed through it, and when the storage of information is complete, all parts of the sensory system are more or less "equipotent." In the typical complex and painstaking experiment carried out by Pribram and Spinelli, a monkey sits down in front of a translucent panel on which either a circle or four vertical stripes are projected. It is trained to press the right half of the panel when it sees the circle or to press the left half when it sees the stripes. The reward is a peanut which drops into a receptacle at his left elbow. Before the experiment, tiny electrodes are implanted in the visual cortex. The comparison of the electrical waves produced during and after the training shows a marked difference. What seems to be most important and unexpected is that from the wave form record it is possible to tell if the monkey saw the circle or the stripes, if it made mistakes or gave correct responses, and whether it *intended* to press the right or the left half of the panel once it was presented with the problem and *before* it initiated an overt response. Since all those electroencephalographic responses originated in the visual cortex, the authors have implied that signals representing experience converge with and modify the afferencies of the visual-input system.

The visual information which the monkey perceived does not represent a pure and simple coding of the light patterns focused on the retina, but rather it represents the result of an integrative process involving influences from other sensory systems. These influences take place at the level of the input phase of the process, and the resulting information, which is already linked to a learned response, becomes distributed over a wide region of the visual cortex. The mode in which this distribution occurs, at least in terms of a working hypothesis, will be discussed in Chapter IV.

Further experiments by Pribram *et al.* have shown that the removal of the cortical areas surrounding the primary visual cortex, areas which are also known as a prestriate cortex,[157a, b, 176, 191] do not interfere significantly on visual discrimination of monkeys so that they can still discriminate at the 86 per cent level at the first testing after surgery. The infero-temporal cortex (one of the areas of the posterior association cortex of primate described above), therefore, is anatomically related to the visual system only by an indirect pathway and functions independently of the primary visual system. The interpretation has been that the infero-temporal cortex works through efferents aimed to control the input within the primary visual system. When the infero-temporal cortex is electrically stimulated, the shape and size of the visual receptive fields of units in the optic nerve change significantly. The effect can be registered electrophysiologically as far as the retina or the cochlear nucleus in the experiments in which the stimulation is limited to the middle areas, which are related with hearing, of the posterior association cortex.

The pathway through which the infero-temporal cortex works in this efferent control of the input within the primary visual system is represented by the superior *colliculus,* a sizable zone in the *putamen,* the anterior commissure, the nucleus medialis dorsalis, the *pulvinar* of the thalamus, the pons, and other areas of the temporal lobe. To quote Pribram: "The inferior temporal cortex (parallel findings are available in the auditory system) seems to work through structures to which motor functions have usually been attributed. It has become evident that even these motor functions are largely controlled via efferents to their receptors, the gamma fibers to the muscle spindles. Information becomes distributed in the sensory projection systems, and the function of the so-called posterior association areas are to organize the input so as to make it memorable. However, this organizing process does not appear to occur within these 'association' areas *per se.* Rather, their effect is exercised down stream on structures heretofore labeled as motor in function. In view of the fact that such control over movement is now recognized to be largely due to the regulation of muscle receptors, it is perhaps not altogether unlikely that other receptor mechanisms, such as the auditory and visual, are also controlled by way of these 'motor' pathways."

The problem of the distribution of the incoming information throughout the brain has been the target of further studies by Sokolow[373] on human and animal habituation. (See page 93.) They have indicated that such a distribution is not only topographical but also chronological. The brain can distribute temporally information for the period necessary to a satisfactory registration. Sokolow's experiments have shown that habituation is not due to neuronal fatigue: in fact, by just lowering the intensity of the stimulus (or even by complete silence, when auditory stimuli are expected), dishabituation and reorientation occur. During reorientation, some physiological concomitants, such as change in the electrical conductivity of the skin, heart, and respiratory rate and electroencephalogram pattern, also change. By measuring them, one can indirectly evaluate reorientation.* Pribram and Bagshaw,[331] by using this experimental method, have shown that when the physiological indicators of the orienting reaction mentioned above are absent, the stimulus, even though perceived, fails to be registered as a memory trace.

---

*Change in those physiological indicators during classical conditioning occurs earlier and earlier as the subject rehearses the situation and anticipates the following events. Anticipation and registration, which represent a chronological distribution of the memory trace, are impaired after the removal of the frontal lobes or the amygdala. The rehearsal-like phenomenon ceases.[330] e

Chapter III

LEARNING AND MEMORY AS BIOLOGICAL PROCESSES

NEUROPHYSIOLOGICAL MODELS OF LEARNING AND MEMORY AND BASIC MECHANISMS OF GENERAL BRAIN FUNCTIONING

Thinking of a model in relationship to learning and memory mechanisms strictly implies having a concept of the mode or ways by which those processes occur. With the gradual development of neurophysiological research, the problems of learning and memory have become an integral part of a more comprehensive, complex, and still partially solved problem of the nature of brain mechanics, of the essence and mechanisms of conscious experience, and of the metapsychic, more than neurologic, problem of the relationship between mind and brain and between psychic phenomena and the functioning of the central nervous system.

The *neuroanatomical approach* to the study of learning and memory as biological phenomena, after having attempted to isolate the sites of the brain where those processes occur and whose damage causes disturbance of those functions, has been overwhelmed by the biological (physiological and biochemical) approach which has attempted to establish a working model of brain functioning from the standpoint of the electrophysiological and chemical properties of the brain tissue. Learning and memory from this point of view may result from anatomical changes occurring at the neuronal level, especially within the synapses between axons and dendrites. Since synapses grow and are also electrophysiologically modifiable with an increased capacity of transmission following repeated activation (See below.), the *synaptic model* appears suitable for understanding the mode by which a transitory process of information registration becomes a permanent process of storage of the memory trace. In this model a specific memory is determined by any number of sites along a neural pathway and by their sequential order of firing. It may also account for the growth of memory with experience even though the number of neurons available for that function declines with age (30% between age of 20 and 80 and 100,000 on an average for each day of adult life[57a]). In addition, in this model the chemical factor is seen as fundamental as far as the chemical mediators of the electrical impulses at the level of the synaptic junctions are concerned, such as, for example, the acetylcholine. But jonic changes at the level of cell membrane both in the neurons and the synapses appear to be, according to recent studies, of fundamental importance *(electrophysiological and electrochemical models)*. The *biochemical or macromolecular model* emphasizes the role of the rearrangement of the molecular structure of neurons as the basic process underlying the permanent storage of the memory trace.

Before discussing in detail the various models of learning and memory mechanisms, a brief outline of brain mechanics in terms of neurophysiological operations is worthy of a concise outline.

Crude information as supplied by the sense organs is gradually shaped into abstract concepts. The first step in this process is *recognition* of a new information as identical to that previously acquired. The second step, which occurs only at the evolutionary level of the human species, is *cognition,* a process by which a concrete concept related to a first-degree, low-level integration in the brain becomes an abstract idea, a concept which includes only the essential elements of the original information. At this higher level of integration the use of verbal symbols in man facilitates abstract conceptualization, such as that which characterizes, for example, philosophical concepts, mathematical equations, and poetical or artistical modes of thought expression. If the role of language is crucial for the abstract type of thinking, practice in learning is essential. The formation of thoughts rather than expressing innate ability, results from a long-lasting experience. Harlow's classical experiments of two decades ago on monkeys, which learned to identify symbols by particular learning sets, have shown that verbalization, as represented by stimuli or signs calling for that learning set that is most appropriate for solving a given problem, is *conditio sine qua non* for the formation of thoughts.[173, 174]

Further support to the role of language in the process of thinking comes from the study of aphasia and deaf-mutism. The study of aphasic patients[38, 155] has shown that a loss of abstracting ability is typical of the condition also known as ataxic aphasia or verbal deafness (which contrasts the motor aphasia or apraxic aphasia characterized by a preserved thinking process). Thinking and language may be disturbed separately from the clinical viewpoint, but neuropathologically, when the internal type of language is impaired, even though the external language as a pure and simple verbalization is not affected, the thought process is disturbed. The electromyographic study of aphasic patients has shown that even when tongue movements are absent in motor aphasia, tongue muscles are electrophysiologically functioning.[60a-1] No thinking disorder can be evidenced in the same patients. Internal language, which is based upon the motor activity of the phonatory muscles, therefore, is essential for the normal operation of thought processes in aphasic patients. On the other hand, no conceptualization and abstraction seem to be possible without satisfactory functioning of the muscles directly or indirectly involved in speech production. "So-called thinking," as Watson[417b] stated in 1920, is nothing more than minute, subvocal contractions of the muscles involved in the production of speech.

The study of deaf-mutes[361] has demonstrated that in the congenital form of deaf-mutism the quality of thinking never goes beyond the concrete type. In the trained form of speech and hearing loss, thinking is less concrete, and some ability to symbolize and conceptualize appear. On the other hand, people who becomes deaf after having learned to speak show no concreteness of thinking. One of the most impressive clinical documentations of the role of language in the process of thought formation is given by the case of Helen Keller, a deaf and blind girl, who was mute, and who gradually developed mental processes by tactile training first and speech formation later on. Not provided with general thoughts, she started thinking only after having learned the spoken language.[225]

The flexibility of verbal thinking, which contrasts to the rigidity of any other form of concrete information in the processes of correlation, combination, and integration of names with other symbols of previous experience, stems from the plasticity of the neural code. This is a set of routine instructions on how to control the direction of flow of the electrical impulses into the neuronal network. The plasticity of the neural code, in turn, contrasts to the rigidity of the genetic code, which is a set of instructions on how to organize the sequence of amino acids to form the enzymes responsible for the synthesis of the biological material. On the basis of those characteristics of the neural and genetic code, one can understand how the mind has been quite stable during the evolution of human species. While its learning ability has remained stable at least for twenty centuries, brain functioning has responded with adequate changes to different environmental conditions. Further knowledge has accumulated impressively through the transfer of acquired information from generation to generation.

The hierarchical organization of human knowledge from the crude information as supplied by the sense organs to that percepted within the specific sensory areas of the cerebral cortex, reflects the hierarchical organization of the human nervous system, first hypothesized by the British neurologist John Hughlings Jackson and still valid today, even though some subcortical structures, such as the reticular core, have been recognized as capable of controlling the highest cortical functions. The image of the pyramid in this hierarchical organization of the nervous system is reversed in the sense that its base is on the higher level (that of the cerebral cortex) and its apex is on the lower level (that of the subcortical structures).

The establishment of a hierarchical level of abstractions and, on a lower functioning, the handling, management, and molding of every bit of information requires a *coding system* similar to that valid in cybernetics and in computer theory and technical design, a system of signals similar to magnetic tapes, records, maps, etc. in which information can be registered, stored, manipulated (computed), and retrieved. The mechanism by which the coding system operates seems to be electrophysiological and biochemical in nature and to consist of the establishment of on-off (excitation-rest) combinations of neuronal units in the form of patterns. While the size and distribution of the pattern of the electrical impulse evoked by the brain cells, the rate of firing, and the number or type of fibers put into excitation account for the quantitative aspect of the information carried out by the brain, the type of that pattern, the location of the receptor cells at the periphery, and the contribution of other neuronal circuits at different hierarchical levels of the nervous system account for the quality of the coded material.[264] At the cortical level the stimulation of neurons is not followed by any negative or positive reinforcement of a given information inherent to a given sensory pathway, and therefore, the coding quality is practically missed. It is strongly represented at the periphery, however. The proper coding of the stimulus, once the end-organ is bypassed, can be assured only partially at the level of the reticulo-limbic system where electrical stimulation is able to produce some positive or negative reinforcement.

The information coded at the periphery in terms of type, intensity, location of the sensory input, etc. should be decoded, after storage in the central nervous system, rerouted, correlated, and integrated with the information formerly coded and already stored in order to give meaning to that information and to translate it into new action. The first mechanism by which decoding of information occurs without loss of specificity along the centripetal moving of the input from the periphery to the cortical centers is that consisting of branching and synapsing of each neuron in the relay chain without arrest or connection in the reticular core. Another mechanism is that by which information decoding occurs with loss of specificity due to a process of a convergence at the level of the reticular core and the limbic system with the final result that it does not allow the conveyance of specific information.

A concept which is fundamental for the understanding of general brain functioning in terms of on-off combinations of conducting neurons is that neurophysiological operations are automatic, selective, and spontaneous. Motor coordination, for example, is controlled by brain centers and nerve pathways even during the state of unconsciousness. This is the case of the epileptic equivalents characterized by psychomotor activity. Dilatation of the pupil in the darkness or after exposure to frightening scenes in hysterical subjects, its narrowing in an illuminated environment, and blood sugar changes due to suggestion are examples of phenomena occurring spontaneously and automatically through specific neuronal pathways without any influence of conscious awareness.

Practically all neurons discharge spontaneously. The precise time of discharge, however, is not predictable. At other times they will not discharge in contrast to the prediction, assuming that they will discharge predictably. By using Burns'[57b] expression, the response of neurons to constant physiological stimuli is stochastic in nature, since it is a random response which cannot be predicted. The concept of the uncertainty of behavior of the central nervous system stems from the spontaneous and unpredictable character of neuronal firing. The computer communication system operates predictably on the basis of input-output mechanism, and utilizes, as the brain does, convergent and divergent productions to retrieve information previously encoded and permanently stored. Even though different as far as the number of functional basic units (transistors in the computer and neurons in the brain),* both computer and human brain functioning emphasize information and a type of operation.[54, 406]

---

*The number of neurons required to retrieve an item of information, such as the name and address of a person, is still unknown. A digital computer, on the other hand, needs about five thousand bits of information to recall that name and address. The most sophisticated computer so far developed contains no more than 150 billion memory bits and occupies a space 32 x 32 feet. Each of the estimated 10-12 billion neurons contained in the gray matter of the cerebral cortex (whose thickness ranges between 0.125 inch[122] and 0.1 inch,[108 c] and whose area has been estimated as 400 sq. in. large) is so small that two hundred cells could be put in a row to match the diameter of a dime. Neurons are formed by hundreds of outlets (through the axon) and inlets (dendrites). The connection takes place at the level of the end-branches of the axon of one cell with the dendrite of another cell. The junctions are called synapses. More precisely this term indicates the gap between the two types of branches coming in contact with each other. It is a cleft of a few Angstroms wide, so that a space less than one millionth of an inch is left between the two structures.[108 c] The first photographic evidence of a complete nerve linkage has been obtained recently by a team of scientists headed by E. R. Lewis, associate professor of Electrical Engineering at the University of California, Berkeley. By using a scanning electron microscope and a specimen from a marine snail, the crucial point, at the end of the nerve fibers, i.e. the synaptic knob, has been shown in three dimensions at a magnification up to 20,000 times life-size. These knobs appear to lie across one another in clusters like a random pile of logs at the point where a large "trunkline" fiber from one neuron meets a similar fiber from another neuron. The knobs seem to have five to six spots firmly attached to other knobs of nerve tissue.

Bioelectricity is the physical phenomenon which is at the basis of the nerve impulse propagation along nerves and muscles (at a rate of about 100 miles per second in a neuronal unit[196, 358b]). The electric current is carried by ions whose movement across the cell membrane has been attributed to rapid and reversible permeability changes of the membrane. Initially interpreted as a diffusion process accounting exclusively for conduction, it has been also interpreted as resulting from the activity of a chemical mediator, especially acetylcholine, which would account for the transmission across the synapses. The transmitter theory of nerve function, however, shows some weakness if one considers the methods of study which have been used to test it, i.e. the combination of classic, pharmacologic methods with electrophysiological techniques. They are considered today rather inadequate for investigating molecular events occurring in excitable membranes. The biochemical approach introduced in the fifties has proved to be more reliable in the attempt to unfold the mysteries of nerve function, even though at the present time more information is needed concerning the mechanism of that functioning at a molecular level.

Acetylcholine, according to current opinion, is no longer considered the trigger which initiates and controls the permeability of cell membrane and ion balance during electrical activity in nerve tissue.[108c, 124, 190, 264, 269a,b] The concentration of potassium ions (with negative charge) on the inside of the cell membrane is twenty times larger than on the outside, and the concentration of sodium ions (with positive charge) on the outside is ten times larger than on the inside.[196] When excitation takes place, cell potential, which in the resting state is about 70 mv,[196] drops; the resistance of the cell membrane decreases, and while potassium ions pass to the outside, sodium ions pass inside the cell. The duration of the excitatory phase is only a fraction of a second, and many discharges may occur within a second. If the cell potential increases, rather than drops, as it occurs under the influence of inhibitory impulses from other neurons, there is no electrical discharge along the cell. The algebraic sum of the opposite stimulations makes the neuron respond in a given way. It has been estimated that when a neuron is stimulated electrically, about eight billion other neurons may respond electrophysiologically within 0.004 seconds.[122]

To quote Nachmanson,[269b] one of the initiators and most experienced investigators of the role of proteins and enzymes in cell function, the picture of the acetylcholine role which best fits the available data is the following: "Excitation leads to the release of AcCh from its bound form in resting condition. It acts as a signal recognized within the membrane by a specific AcCh-receptor protein.

The concept of predictability of neuronal functioning became widely accepted about two decades ago because by experimenting generally on nerves physically separated from their organisms, it became apparent that those nerves responded only when stimulated by the experimenter. Modern research, based on the introduction of statistics for the study of stochastic systems and on the use of microelectrode recording of the cortical electrical response, has led to the reversal of that concept, i.e. the unpredictability of neuronal functioning. It should be borne in mind, however, that this concept is all but absolute in the sense that on the "noisy" background of an unpredictable average frequency of neuronal firing, which does not "tell" when its parameters are able to influence the behavior of other neurons and therefore cause physiological changes, there are more or less predictable responses of the system which are the true physiological important responses of the central nervous system. From what has been said, it appears clear that the general purpose electronic computer communicating system fits better as an analogue for

---

The reaction induces a conformational change of the protein, thereby possibly releasing $Ca+$ ions bound to the protein. Calcium ions are involved in the excitability of nerve and muscle fibers which become inexcitable in the absence of divalent cations and are distinguished from other divalent cations by several remarkable features and properties. Their release may induce further conformational changes of phospholipids and other polyelectrolytes. The end result of the sequence of chemical reactions is the change of membrane permeability to ions, a change that permits the movements of many thousand of ions, possibly as many as 20,000 to 40,000 in each direction per molecule of AcCh released. These reactions thus act as typical amplifiers of the signal given by AcCh. Acetylcholinesterase rapidly hydrolizes AcCh, thereby permitting the return of the receptor protein to its original conformation and reestablishing the barrier for the ion movements."

"Acetylcholine in its bound form and the two proteins reacting directly with the AcCh released, receptor and esterase, are presumably linked together structurally as well as functionally and form a protein assembly in the excitable membrane in a way comparable with other enzyme systems—for example, the electron transfer system in mitochondrial membranes. The structural organization of the system may account for the efficiency, the precision, and the speed of the events in the membrane during electrical activity. While the essential role of Ca_2^+ ions in the permeability changes of excitable membranes appears likely, their release requires a specific control mechanism. Among the cell components, only proteins are known to have the ability to recognize specific ligands and thereby provide the proper control for initiating and terminating a specific cell function."[269b]

the study of the central nervous system than the classical analogue of the telephone switchboard.

Since the firing of a single neuron is not followed by the firing of the entire network in which it is located, multiple firing by several neurons (a sort of summating effect) is required for the initiation of function in the net. This process often causes inhibition of the response of adjacent neurons. Therefore, a neuronal network may be better understood in terms of a floating point notion rather than of a specific neuroanatomic space.

That the basis of brain functioning in general and of the mechanisms of learning and memory specifically is the formation of patterns of on-off combinations among conducting neuronal units is also accepted by those investigators[60a-1, 244] who believe that the activity of the central nervous system takes place through a continuous, automatic activity of neurons within specific centripetal and centrifugal pathways with the cooperation of aspecific afferencies from muscle proprioceptors and other regions of the body so that a given experiential information may be recognized as a part of the physical personality of the individual. This concept of brain functioning, in which no particular and necessary emphasis is given to closed loops of neurons reactivating themselves by previous stimulation putting them in a pattern form, points to the periphery as indispensable for perception of the external world; it gives at least the same emphasis to the rebounding from central to peripheral and back to central pathways and centers for the apperception of the external and internal reality as it is presented in crude terms of perceptive experience.

The Italian neurologist, Vito Maria Buscaino,[60a-1] has been the originator and promulgator of this model of "brain mechanics" (to use an expression of another famous Italian neurologist, Leonardo Bianchi), on the basis of his original studies of the neurobiology of vision about three decades ago, confirmed and extended especially by his school in Naples. In the case of vision, for example, perception of form results from the proprioceptive function of the ocular muscles. In the case of phonation, internal language, i.e. that which is not verbally expressed but still takes place on the basis of a mental word representation, is associated with the activity of the laryngeal and the tongue muscles, clearly demonstrable by electromyography.

V. M. Buscaino has envisaged a unifying mechanism of brain functioning consisting of a complex, selective, desynchronized activity of chains of neurons in relationship to specific afferencies (sense organs) and aspecific afferencies (proprioceptors). The activity would take place through well-defined nerve pathways from the periphery to the cortical centers, and vice versa, and secondarily through centro-peripheral circuits of a "feedback" type responsible for the continuous reactivation of the experiential information. To quote G. A. Buscaino,[59] who recently has synthesized the concept of brain functioning of his father and teacher V. M. Buscaino: ". . . according to our school consciousness is not only a state of wakefulness, nor is it the expression of activity in a single region of the nervous system; it is the outcome of the selective and adequate activity of at least three complex neuronic systems among the innumerable ones which ten billion cerebral neurons allow us to conceive. The fulfillment of an act of complete consciousness (e. g. an elementary idea both conceived or expressed) consists, according to V. M. Buscaino, of: the selective neuromuscular activity of special circuits going from the cortex to the muscular periphery (vocal in this case) or to any other sensitive sensory systems, and from the periphrery again to the cortical centers: informing other circuits of what is going on in that particular circuit in order to avoid contemporaneous interference of activity from other sensitive-sensory systems; the participation of mechanisms of the body image, so that the event is recognized as forming part of the individual personality."

"Besides pointing out that the peripheral functioning is indispensable to perceptions, and especially to the visual and auditory one of the external world, the doctrine underlines the concept of the centro-peripheral functioning of the same sensory organs during visual and auditory representations, and of those depending on language (language which is written, read, spoken or heard) for internal language and hence for abstract thought in the wider sense of the word. And there exists a vast documentation concerning the existence of these centro-peripheral pathways at the retina, eye muscles, cochlea, internal ear muscles, those of the tongue, etc. (s. V. M. Buscaino)."

"When selective activity is absent because all the neurons are working at the same time on in a very regular way, or worse, still they are working synchronously, the state of consciousness does not take place (e.g. a generalized convulsive seizure)."

"Moreover, it is indispensable to state that adequate eye movements which actually occur are necessary to perceptions of form; whereas peripheral participation in the corresponding muscular region are essential for representation of form and therefore of movement."

"From the enormous quantity of data collected by V. M. Buscaino (1946, 1962, 1963) we may conclude that there is no thought which does not flow into the motor periphery; no visual image of movement which is not accompanied by contractions or electric variations of the eye muscles, there is no 'minded' image of a moving limb which is unaccompanied by very slight motor variations in the motor periphery or at least by electric peripheral modifications in the muscular territory 'present in the mind.' Dreaming is a state of wakefulness during sleep; it is, in a way, a form of thinking during sleep. During the phase which corresponds to dream, the desynchronization of the electroencephalogram is accompanied by a flow of stimuli through the centroperipheral pathways, toward the 'sleeping' periphery and this, without the sleeper being aware of it, it is reactivated and guides to the centres the same stimuli which influence our sensory systems during wakefulness, obviously arising the same reactions (emotional, reflexive, neurovegetative) which are recognized, detected and felt in the form of dreams."

"More exactly, as there exist some very well-known centroperipheral pathways capable of reactivating the periphery (motor, sensitive and sensory) by centrifugal stimulations (representations), it is natural that the selective functioning of one of these pathways, in our case the eye movements associated with a retinal participation, reactivates the periphery as though the stimuli really came from the external world (REM phase). These stimuli sent to the analyzer and associative centers, in our case those of the striated and parastriated regions, while the subject is sleeping, provoke a more or less perfect recognition of them, cause their transformation into more or less exact visual images, and in short condition the appearance of dreaming."

"Interference from other neuronic complexes functioning at the same time but in a less active way could explain the fact that many dream representations are mixed up with heterogeneous elements in a confusion of almost foolish images."

"Observation of the persistence of REM's in decorticated cats, in subjects with syndrome of chronic decortication and decerebration or with cortical blindness or Belint's paralysis, are not contrary to this centroperipheral interpretation of dreaming."[59]

A remarkable contribution of the neurosciences to the understanding of brain functioning in general, other than to the clarification of some aspects of learning and memory mechanisms, has been the emphasis placed by the neurophysiological research on an individual mode of thinking which becomes shaped during the growth of the individual rather than onto a universal mode of thinking as it was believed in ancient time. As a matter of fact, it has been proved that the input signals can be modified in the brain even before they reach the specific sensory areas of the cortex, and that this alteration of sensory stimuli is due to the prewired organization of the nervous system of each individual but is also significantly influenced by learning experiences. Experience, in other words, molds neurophysiological mechanisms, even those which appear more stable and closely depending upon genetic and biochemical factors. The central nervous system is not only the site where passive interconnecting functions occur, but also, and perhaps primarily, a structure allowing an active function upon varied incoming sensory stimuli.

The classical experiment carried out in 1956 by the Mexican neurophysiologist Hernandez-Péon *et al.*[182] showed that the action potential of the cochlear nucleus in the cat is significantly reduced if a visual stimulus (a mouse) or an olfactory or visual stimuli (a fish) are presented. A given sensory function, in other words, becomes inhibited when it is competing with another one. Brain centers are not only subjected to environmental stimulation, but actively operate even before the stimulation and control the input coming from the body receptors. Hernandez-Péon has confirmed the results of his study in humans. During arithmetical calculations, for example, the action potential recorded from visual input appears remarkably reduced. More recently the same investigator has shown that the action potential, evoked from the nucleus gracilis through the stimulation of the dorsal column and evoked from the lateral geniculate body and the visual cortex through the stimulation of the auditory and visual areas of the brain, is depressed or abolished following stimulation of the reticular core, perhaps by inhibition of the peripheral sensitive and sensorial "relay."

Galambos[137a, b] has shown that in the auditory cortex of the cat neuronal units respond electrically to acoustic input only if the cat focuses its attention on that input. He has called those neurons "cells of attention" since they enter into action only when the actual stimuli interest the animal. More recently Galambos[137c] has also found that the electroencephalographic response to clicks from monkeys, subjected to an annoying air puff on their faces while they are hearing the click, spreads over the cortex far away from the auditory pathway and that this occurs only when the air puff is stopped. By pairing the click with different sensory events, such as a flash of light or a sugar pill, the response obtained involves a cortical area well beyond that corresponding to the primary stimulation. The animal senses the stimulus differently than before because of the consequent involvement of that area of the brain which is markedly charged with emotional content because of the contribution of the reticulo-limbic system.

Another interesting finding by Jouvet *et al.*[216] is that the action potential of the thalamic nuclei becomes reinforced after repeated stimulation if the subject focuses his attention on the stimuli, for example by counting them. Those authors also showed that the action potential decreases if the subject is distracted, for example by listening to music or by doing a mathematical calculation, or is indeed nonexistent if repeated clicks are presented to an animal whose interest is not focused on them.

Other studies by Dewson[98] and Gerbrandt[145] have further supported the concept that modification of the sensory signals takes place at the input phase. In Gerbrandt's experiment, taken as an example, the auditory system has been investigated. A monkey sitting inside a box, which can be opened to allow him to see outside, is stimulated through an electrode placed in the lateral geniculate nucleus (the "relay" station within the visual input system), and the electrical activity of the visual cortex is recorded. The response appears small when the box is closed, large when open. In the former instance, and only in that, the electrical response of the visual cortex may increase by stimulating the inferior temporal association cortex.

Pribram *et al.*[330c] have shown that signals representing experience converge with and modify the input before they reach the specific sensory areas of the cortex. The information inherent to the input becomes distributed over a large cortical area rather than remaining localized to a specific sensory area. This process favors the integration between the specific input and the other numerous signals from contiguous regions of the cortex which are already linked to learned experience. Rather than a true "replica" of the external environment, the sensory system provides information which is representative of it, but which is also highly integrated with other sensory and emotionally colored signals. The investigation of Pribram *et al.*, which has been discussed in detail in Chapter II, concerning the localization of learning and memory in the brain, points to the fact that even receptor activity is controlled by the cerebral cortex through a complex system of fibers, some leaving the sensory cortex with a true efferent function, others reaching the motor cortex with a true afferent function. Even a single spinal reflex does not appear as simple as traditionally known, since it is influenced by central excitatory as well as inhibitory impulses. Recent experiments by Jaspers[211] have shown that the conditioned response may occur bilaterally even though the conditioning occurred unilaterally.

All the data reported above, most of which concern the visual system and therefore are not necessarily indicative of similar phenomena in other sensory input systems, directly or indirectly indicate that perception may be modified by past experience, expectation, and purposes. To quote testually R. B. Livingston[257]: "Each person perceives the world through his own set of 'filters' or 'lenses' which are as unlikely to be completely shared by another person as are fingerprints." "If you and I witness the same event and come away with different testimonies, according to the Cartesian view I would have to assume one of two things: 1. that you are unable to master the psychologic implications of what you had seen or 2. that you were lying, distorting in favor of whatever narrow interests may motivate you. But now we raise a third possibility; you may not have central nervous access to understand data, it is filtered out or distorted before it even got to a center of active appreciation. In conclusion, rather than a universal mode of thinking, many modes would exist in relationship to individual experience and indoctrination which seems to reach the peak at about 12 years of age." According to Livingston,[257] "Physiological different brains are made, not born." "Better technology will probably discover some day, perhaps at a molecular level, what their anatomical differences are. In the 300 years, since Descartes, men have tried to appreciate the world objectively, but our neurological work indicates that it can't be done."

ELECTROPHYSIOLOGICAL MODEL OF LEARNING AND MEMORY

From the neurophysiological point of view, learning and memory mechanisms were more hypothetically than factually understood until the late twenties when Karl Lashley[250c] experimentally demonstrated than no memory impairment or loss occurs following so deep and extensive incisions throughout the cerebral cortex that the connecting pathways between neurons were presumably interrupted in the laboratory animals. (See Chapter II.) At that time the so-called pathway theory of brain functioning, resulting from the investigations of conditioned responses, prevailed in the neurophysiological thinking. The brain was considered as a relay organ between receptors and effectors so that conditioned responses could easily take place. The morphological and topographical arrangements of brain cells, with their axons and dendrites branching and connecting with each other in a very complex way and so extensively spread over that they appear indeed redundant, support the concept that the basic function of neurons is to transmit information and allow communication. One should not be surprised that one of the early models of brain functioning was that of a passive receiver and transmitter of information; the brain was thought simply to allow the establishment and maintenance of connections like a telephone exchange center.

However, the attempts to demonstrate specific pathways in the brain, which would be responsible for stimulus-response connections and for the association of new stimuli with already established memory traces, failed.[250a-d, 330a] On the other hand, learning may occur simply by observation rather than by association.[70, 214, 355, 372, 402 a, b] (See Chapter II.) The strictly linear pathway theory of brain functioning, therefore, gradually appeared less significant with respect to the so-called field theory which was initially supported by Lashley's research[28] and appeared too rigid to explain the fundamental characteristics of brain functioning, i.e. its plasticity. The quantity of the cortical tissue experimentally cut off became more significant than its specific location.[250a] The implication was not only that each sensory system of the brain is provided with a large functional reserve, widely distributed through the cortex, but also that the pattern of neuronal excitation more than the involvement of particular neurons is essential to assure the state of conscious awareness and to account for learning and memory processes.

In order to recognize the meaning of an advertising sign formed by a bank of bulbs, it is necessary that a given number of bulbs are lit in a pattern out of the remaining bulbs which remain dark. The elements turned on or off could be variant, but that particular meaningful and recognizable combination or pattern of lit bulbs should be the same in order to produce that particular information.* The sixteen strokes per second which a skilled musician is able to make also represents, according to Lashley, a too rapid performance for being accounted for on the basis of the stimulus-response mechanism. This is also the case of ordinary speech when it rolls out in an organized fashion anytime a remark is made to express an idea.

At this stage of evolution of the neurophysiological thinking about brain mechanics and the modes and ways by which learning and memory process occur, the Canadian psychologist, Donald G. Hebb formulated in 1947 an electrophysiological model of brain functioning based upon a particular type of patterned modality of neuronal stimulation.

Hebb[178] noted that a short-acting (1-2 seconds) electrical stimulation of an area of the cerebral cortex causes a prolonged (minutes or even hours occasionally) rhythmical production of an action potential. Hebb interpreted the phenomenon as resulting from web-like, multiple neuronal connections allowing the passage of the nerve impulses again and again through the same synapses in a circular fashion till the circuit fatigues and the circular motion ceases, in a way somewhat similar to the pattern of the electrical response described by Lorente De No'[258] to explain how a neural process initiated in a given area of the brain can self-propagate. Lorente De No' called "reverberating arcs" the circular pathways of that neural propagation. Hebb called

---

*Lashley's concept that the pattern of excitation rather than the involvement of particular neurons is crucial for brain functioning in general and for learning and memory processes specifically shows marked similarity with the concept expressed by the Italian neurologist Vito Maria Buscaino, [60 a-c] three decades ago. His original statement says[60 h]: "Se tutti i neuroni *funzionano contemporaneamente*, attivita' selettiva non ne risulta e quindi attivita' cosciente non ne puo' seguire, alla stessa maniera, per fare un paragone dimostrativo, per cui, al pianoforte, una melodia spunta se si abbassano i tasti isolatamente all'incirca, non quando si abbassano *tutti* contemporaneamente. Ora nello stato di attivita' cosciente la corteccia elettroencefalograficamente risulta desincronizzata, mentre e' tipicamente sincronizzata nello stato di sonno. Quando poi durante il sonno l'attivita' cerebrale si desincronizza-sia per impulsi centro-periferico-centrali iniziantisi nella corteccia (Rubino, Ag.), sia per impulsi perifero-centro-periferici iniziantisi nel tronco cerebrale (Buscaino, G. A.)—spunta quel tipo particolare di attivita' psichica che costituisce il sogno." "Il sogno e' un'allucinazione durante il sonno." "L'allucinazione e' un sogno in veglia."[60]

"cell assemblies" the closed loops of activated neurons and "phase sequences" the more complex neuronal networks resulting from the connection of several cell assemblies.* More recently the term *engram* has become popular among neurophysiologists to indicate a neuronal pattern of an acquired skilled act.

In his dual-trace model of memory briefly discussed in Chapter I, Hebb[178] thought that the duration of the electrophysiological effect of a stimulus in the brain was due to an after-discharge and reverberatory cycle within the neuronal circuits and that this process would account for the initial phase of registration of the experiential information *(Hebb's semiautonomous cell assemblies theory)*. The process is of a short duration because of the spontaneous decay due to neuronal fatigue and the consequent cessation of the circular motion of the electrical impulses within the closed loop of neurons. The establishment of a more durable memory trace during the so-called phase of consolidation of memory would result from a structural change in the neuronal network promoted by the activity trace memory. Hebb himself recognized in his experiments of the immediate recall of nine digits that the retrieval could not be subserved by an activity trace since its duration was too short to explain the cumulative learning effect.[178] A structural

---

*The reverberating circuit is a subtype of several *electrophysiological circuits* which operate in the central nervous system of man and animals. The most important is the *repetitive firing circuit.* One of its subtypes is that ocurring along chains of neurons in which the incoming stimulus activates each neuron in succession. The other type, the *reverberating circuit* mentioned above, occurs in a pool of neurons and functions in such a way that the stimulus goes around in a circle, and the oscillation usually ceases when neurons become fatigued. A typical example of this sort of neuronal activity is that responsible for thought process and respiratory rhythm. The other two types of neuronal circuits are the *diverging circuits* and the *converging circuits.* The former, which is the simpler one, is characterized by the fact that the nerve fiber of each neuron divides many times, and few impulses enter the neuronal pool, while many others leave it. The nervous control of muscular activity is accomplished through this type of circuit. The converging circuit is that in which the overall effect of its stimulation results from an integrative process involving different types of stimuli coming from several directions with a contribution of factors, such as the basic excitability threshold of neurons as well as the number of inhibitory impulses reaching the circuit and the presence of diverging circuits within the neuronal pool.

change in the neuronal web was then considered as indispensable for the consolidation of the memory trace.

That a sort of physical change occurs at the level of synapses during the passage of nerve impulses was postulated at the end of the 18th century by the Italian neurologist E. Tanzi. While it was later experimentally demonstrated that synaptic function can be affected by excessive use or disuse, it was still questionable that these changes occur during the establishment of learning and memory. Credit should be given to the American psychologist Anthony J. Deutsch[95] for having proved in the fifties that the physical change underlying those processes is essentially the alteration of the transmission efficiency of the synapses. He succeeded in demonstrating that memory registration and the permanent storage of information can be influenced by changing the anatomo-physiological state of synapses through direct or indirect modification of the concentration of the acetylcholine. "Post-tetanic potentiation" of synapses, which means that inter-neuronal connections become facilitated to transmit the electrical impulse after stimulation, is one modality of the phenomenon.[124] An alternate mechanism may be "cell re-excitation" through an interconnection between the axon and the dendrites of the same neuronal unit.[123, 190]

On the other hand, the change which can alter the response of synapses may be structural or molecular as well. It has been shown, for example, that the end-bulbs of the nerve fibers swell as a consequence of activity.[196] Ion displacement across the membrane of the nerve fiber has been found to change the polarization and the inherent electrical potential of that membrane. The occurrence of those phenomena at the level of the synaptic junctions may facilitate or make more difficult the transmission of the electrical impulses through the nerve fibers.[108a-c, 122, 124, 196] If the structural and physico-chemical state of the synapses and their inherent functional performance appear to be a critical factor for the direct transmission of nerve impulses, the functional state of the neighboring neurons connected with the reverberating circuits and the timing activity which could affect each of them appear also to be significant factors for the total functioning of the neuronal networks.

The persevering activity of neurons upon which Hebb's electro-physiological model of learning and memory and the consolidation process as well are based have an adequate experimental support in Duncan's study first[106] and in numerous other investigations later on. Rats thought a conditioned avoidance response and an electrical shock given at different time intervals have shown loss of retention of the conditioned response which was greater as the time interval shortened between the learning experience and the shock. Apparently, the electroshock broke the natural persevering process of the nerve cells. This has been confirmed experimentally by many investigators, Hebb included. Not only by electroshock, but also by a number of other procedures were they able to disrupt the continuing electrical activity of the involved neurons, such as hibernation, hypoxia, and head trauma. [44, 67, 106, 144a,c, 273-275, 313, 419] Sleep or anesthesia only slow down the electrical activity of the brain and do not significantly affect memory function.[144a]

In Gerard's experiment,[144a] shock given one minute after the training of hamsters, which learned to run in a maze to get a reward, destroyed learning completely. Treatment given one hour later impaired learning moderately, and treatment given four hours later did not alter it at all. Other hamsters trained similarly were cooled to a body temperature of −40°F. (at which temperature no electrical activity is picked up by electrodes implanted in the brain) or were exposed to nitrogen for two hours and then tested, after recovery, for the retention of the learned experience. The result was that the hamsters recalled the task.

More recently Bovet and Oliverio[44] have duplicated Duncan and Gerard's experiments by using longer training schedules (50 trials with intervals of 24 hours). Memory loss due to electric shock was noted only if the shock was administered two minutes after the end of the session. The analysis of the learning curves has also shown a distinct effect of electroshock on short-term memory, i.e. decrement of memory function related especially to the initial curve of performance between the end of one session and the beginning of the following one, as well as a marked variation (enhancement or detriment) of memory function between two consecutive sessions in groups of mice of different ages. Adult mice (60 days old) perform better than younger (21 days) or older mice (18-360 days). Memory consolidation takes place in adults while decay occurs in young and old mice.

The experiments of McGaugh *et al.* on drug attenuation of retrograde amnesia due to electroshock[273, 274] are also significant in contributing to a better understanding of the mechanisms by which transient memory traces become permanent and of the mode in which some stimulant drugs influence memory function. The initial experiments tested the hypothesis that those drugs may enhance learning by accelerating the rate at which memory traces become consolidated into definitive memories. The retrograde amnesia caused by electroshock was expected to be prevented or attenuated by administration of strychnine or picrotoxin just before or just after the training task. The shock was given a few minutes after the training and the administration of the stimulant drug. Testing on the training task was given twenty-five hours after the shock. The results supported the predictions. Retrograde amnesia was attenuated by the stimulant drugs.

In further experiments in which a single exposure was used as a learning test (one-trial inhibitory test) it became clear that some memory of the learned task persisted when the administration of strychnine took place after the electroshock. The explanation that strychnine affects learning by accelerating the process of memory consolidation appeared insufficient since the drug favored the retention of the learned task even if given after, rather than before, the electroshock. The experiments in which strychnine was administered at various intervals after the electroshock have shown that the longer the interval between the drug and the shock, the less the effect of the drug in improving memory, and it even fails to do that if injected nine hours after the shock. The interpretation of McGaugh *et al.*[273c] was that memory consolidation includes two different phases, the first one consisting of the formations of patterns of firing neuronal units, the second consisting of "empatterning" the memory traces into the coding system formed essentially by that pattern. The retrograde amnesia due to electroshock, which is still evident if the shock is given after eight seconds, i.e following the complete formation of the neuronal pattern, seems to be due to the blockage of the second stage of memory function. The attenuation of retrograde amnesia due to electroshock by stimulant drugs such as strychnine and picrotoxine appears to be caused by interference with the second stage of memory function.

Other experiments by Misanin *et al.*[288] have demonstrated that memory is disrupted by electroshock even twenty-fours hours after training, provided that the memory trace is reactivated immediately prior to the electroshock. A typical retrograde amnesia of a conditioned fear response was produced in rats which received an electroconvulsive shock immediately after conditioning. The authors inferred that electroshock may affect memory not only by disrupting initial consolidation, but also by affecting traces which are in transit from long-term storage into active form of memory. The temporal variable itself, as a primary determinant of the amnesic event of electroshock, appears to be of a lesser significance for the understanding of retrograde amnesia. With respect to the state of change of the memory trace system at the time the electroconvulsive treatment is given in the experiments of Misanin *et al.*,[288] electroshock given immediately after the learning event may or may not have interfered with the long-term storage of the memory for that event or with the elaboration of memory necessary for subsequent retrieval. It did interfere in either case with memory when the trace was in transition from the state of active to that of stored memory in the first case or in transit from one level of accessibility to another in the latter case. Similarly, retrograde amnesia due to electroshock after reactivation of the memory trace may be due to the interference with the trace in transit from stored to active memory.

More recent experiments by Dawson and McGaugh[89] have not confirmed the data and conclusions of Misanin *et al.* Further investigation, therefore, is needed for better understanding of the effects of electroshock on memory function, especially as far as the consolidation of the initial as well as of the reactivated memory traces is concerned. By and large, however, the body of research discussed above has provided adequate support to the so-called consolidation theory of memory function according to which short-term memory is a necessary step for the establishment of a well-consolidated, stable, and enduring memory trace. Short-term memory, in fact, is essentially the expression of an electrophysiological event involving reverberating circuits of neurons.

The experiments of Agranoff *et al.*[6] during the past few years do not appear to support this view, but rather to disprove the functional significance of short-term memory as an electrophysiological process necessary for the permanent storage of the memory trace. This problem will be discussed in Chapter III. At this point it is just interesting to note that evidence has been given by those investigators that the permanent storage of information may also result from a static event, biochemical or macromolecular in nature, and not necessarily from a dynamic, electrophysiological event. Memory consolidation may be prevented by injection of protein synthesis inhibitors, provided however that a given time elapses between the learning experience and the administration of the drug. The consolidation process of memory function, evidently, needs time to take place, but it does not depend necessarily upon an electrophysiological process of neuronal firing, which conversely seems to be necessary for the establishment of short-term memory. Anyway, further investigation should ascertain if the classical procedures which obliterate memory, such as electroshock, hypoxia, hibernation, etc. affect short-term memory, long-term memory, or both.

Albert's experiments[8b] have shown that memory consolidation can be accelerated or slowed down respectively by anodal or cathodal polarization of an area of the cerebral cortex and that the former is capable to restore the memory of rats lost by excessive slowing down of the consolidation rate. One can infer that memory consolidation may be initiated "between" neurons but must be carried out "within" individual neurons. The notion of this concept is particularly significant with respect to the biochemical model of learning and memory which will be discussed below.

Some of the investigations in which the effects of the electroshock and the stimulant drugs were used in an attempt to unfold the mechanisms of registration and retention of experiential information are particularly interesting with respect to a new aspect of memory function, i.e. that of being not only time-dependent in general,[273c] but also dependent upon a specific time of day. Stephens[385] has noted that the retention of an inhibitory training is stronger in rats if the training is given during the night, at which time (exactly at 9 P.M.) some body functions in rodents, such as body temperature and motor activity, reach their peak during a twenty-four hour period; those animals all essentially nocturnal. McGaugh *et al.*[273a-c] have also noted that the retrograde amnesia due to electroshock is surprisingly more pronounced in the animals at the peak of their metabolic activity when the blood concentration of adrenal steroids is also at the highest peak. In other words, the relationship between amnesia because of electroshock and because of metabolic activity is direct, while that between memory consolidation and metabolic activity is inverse. Support to these observations is also given by Stroebel's experiments[387] which suggest that certain emotional conditioning might show a time-lock—linking through the relationship of memory function and biological time of the day during which the conditioning was experimentally allowed.

Another interesting trend of research in the study of the neurophysiological mechanisms of learning and similar behavioral changes in laboratory animals is that which has recently focused attention on the electrophysiological analysis at the cellular level of elementary forms of learning such as *habituation* and *dishabituation*. (See also page 69.) Pinsker et al.[324] of the New York University and the Public Health Research Institute of the City of New York have examined habituation and dishabituation of the gill-withdrawal reflex in *Aplysia,* a marine mollusk whose behavior may be modified experimentally. This type of reflex, which easily undergoes habituation, occurs as a part of a larger defensive withdrawal response that is triggered by a potentially noxious tactile stimulus controlled by the abdominal ganglion of the mollusk. Since the effectiveness of defensive reflexes results from the rapidity of action, the neural circuitry responsible for them is relatively simple, i.e. is assured by a few synaptic junctions. The abdominal ganglion of *Aplysia* contains a few nerve cells whose size allows the penetration of microelectrodes for direct stimulation and recording of synaptic potentials. The reflex withdrawal of the *Aplysia* gill may be elicited by stimulation of a receptive field not including the gill itself, thus minimizing the interference of local peripheral reflexes. Further advantage is that the motor responses of the gill may also be elicited spontaneously in relation to the endogenous activity of the ganglion neurons, thus serving as a potential model for numerous more complex behavioral reactions involving stimulus pairing or pairing of a spontaneous response with a reinforcing stimulus.[324]

The initial results by Pinsker *et al.*[324] have shown that when the gill-withdrawal reflex is repeatedly evoked by a tactile stimulus to the siphon or mantle shelf, the amplitude of the response decreases because of the habituation and spontaneously recovers during the rest period. The amplitude of the habituated response is facilitated by the presentation of a strong tactile stimulus to another part of the animal (dishabituation). The authors have also noted habituation of the dishabituatory stimulus with repeated presentations, greater habituation with short rather than long interstimulus intervals and greater habituation with weak rather than strong stimuli. These features are characteristics of habituation in *Aplysia,* as it has been also observed by other authors.[324] Other features not characteristic of *Aplysia* have also been noted occasionally, i.e. greater habituation with repeated periods of habituation and recovery, generalization of habituation to a stimulus in another part of the receptive field, and prolongation of recovery following additional stimulation after the response has decremented to an asymptote.

Further studies by Kupfermann *et al.*[245] have examined the neuronal correlates of habituation and dishabituation of the gill-withdrawal reflex in *Aplysia* by intracellular recording in identified gill motor neurons in the abdominal ganglion of a semi-intact preparation of *Aplysia* while behavior responses of the gill were simultaneously recorded. The results have shown that habituation and dishabituation are not due to peripheral changes in either the sensory receptors or the gill musculature, but are caused by changes in the amplitude of the excitatory synaptic potentials produced at the gill motor neurons. Thus, habituation and dishabituation of the defensive gill-withdrawal reflex in *Aplysia* are central neurological processes. Habituation results directly from a decrease of the excitatory synaptic potential at the gill motor neurons, whereas dishabituation is due to an increase in this potential.

Finally, the experiments of Castellucci *et al.*[66] have clarified the mechanisms of the excitatory postsynaptic potential decrement. By simultaneous intracellular recording from both the sensory neurons and one of the main identified motor neurons from an isolated abdominal ganglion connected to a piece of skin from the tactile receptive field of the *Aplysia* gill, the withdrawal reflex has been reduced to its monosynaptic components. The monosynaptic excitatory postsynaptic potentials have shown a profound low-frequency depression when repeatedly elicted, and they have shown heterosynaptic facilitation following the application of a strong stimulus to another pathway. Both habituation and dishabituation, consequently, can be explained by changes in the efficacy of specific excitatory synapses.

In conclusion, the experimental data discussed above, by describing behavior parameters of habituation and dishabituation of the gill-withdrawal reflex in the intact *Aplysia* and by providing evidence of their cellular correlates in semi-intact preparations of the same mollusk, indicate that habituation and dishabituation involve changes in the effectiveness of a specific set of central excitatory synapses between the sensory and motor neurons. These changes result from homosynaptic depression and heterosynaptic facilitation respectively. Thus, the relevance of synaptic plasticity to a specific instance of behavioral modification is demonstrated.

BIOCHEMICAL OR MACROMOLECULAR MODEL OF LEARNING AND MEMORY

The mystery of the mechanism by which memory may last even a lifetime has always fascinated scientists and laymen as well.

From the standpoint of a biological permanent alteration of the nerve cells which may account for long-term memory, even though the life time permanence is biochemical in nature, attention has been focused initially on macromolecular changes in the brain cells as the depository of the definitely stored information. Embryonic aspects of this concept may be found from the 19th century in the essays by the Belgian philosopher and mathematician Joseph L. Delboeuf[91] and by the British biologist Thomas H. Huxley. Only in the late forties and early fifties, however, did the growth of the biological theory of learning and memory speed up, taking advantage of the unfolding of the biochemical mechanisms of the imprinting and transmission of genetical information based essentially on the role played by the macromolecules of nucleic acids.* In 1947, the two American psychologists Ward Halstead and Joseph Katz,[171, 172] of the University of Chicago, first presented their theory of the biochemical mechanism of learning and memory within the frame of reference of a complex process also involving electrophysiological events more apt to explain the initial interaction between neurons, and therefore, the mechanism of the initial registration and the short-term retention of the memory trace. Their study will be discussed below.

At this point emphasis should be placed on some data which have stimulated the experimental testing of the new biochemical hypothesis of learning and memory. It was shown, for example, that the paramecia of the infusory family (cells whose membranes

---

*Deoxyribonucleic acid (DNA) exists both in the nucleus (to form the twenty-three pairs of chromosomes which carry the genes of heredity) and free in the cytoplasm. Nucleic DNA can code and transmit from one generation to another the instruction of building up the new organism. Its development takes place according to plans laid down in the pattern of the nucleotide bases (adenine, guanine, cytosine, and thymine) located along the DNA molecules. The mechanism involved in the process of development of the organism is decoding the genetic information. Ribonucleic acid (RNA) is contained in the nucleus as well as in the cytoplasm of the cell, specifically in the cytoplasmic structure identified as mythocondria and ribosomes. Its molecules are patterned after DNA molecules and serve essentially as messengers from the nucleus to the cytoplasm (messenger-RNA) and finally to control protein synthesis in the cell.

have electrical properties similar to those of nerve cells) can learn to cling to a platinum wire.[143] Another interesting finding was that the cells of a rat brain can be conditioned to increase their rate of firing by stimulating the reward center in the hypothalamus just after the nerve cells have fired spontaneously, thus indicating that they behave as if they had learned to fire faster. [302, 303] The possibility was taken into account that the synthesis of new protein within the cell would occur during the learning experience and represent the material in which the memory trace would be permanently stored in brain tissue.[43, 49, 78, 101, 136a, b, 196, 247, 249] Memory consolidation, in other words, was thought to be possible on the basis of a static process not necessarily requiring the dynamic electrophysiological event characterizing the phase of short-term memory.

The triggering factor for the development of the biochemical model of learning and memory has been the discovery that the total stimulation the nerve cells receive, i.e., their learning experience, is the reason for their RNA concentration being the highest of any of the other cells of the body.[202b] It increases progressively from birth to about forty years of age, at which time it has been estimated that about 20 million RNA molecules are contained in each neuron and that about 100,000 proteins become shaped according to the RNA pattern.[14] That discovery was one of the most significant results obtained about one decade ago by the Swedish neurophysiologist Holger Hydén and his co-workers in a series of most sophisticated experiments of the microdissection of isolated neurons followed by biomicroscopical observation and chemical analysis.[201b]

Neurons, as it is well known, do not usually divide in adult life, and DNA is rather metabolically stable, thus appearing well qualified for being the depository of learned information as well as of genetic information. However, the attention of the investigators was focused initially and predominantly on molecules which are more plastic and susceptible to change, such as RNA or protein molecules. Studies have been carried out, therefore, more on DNA-dependent RNA synthesis than on DNA synthesis itself.

Hydén also made the interesting observation that the RNA concentration in the neurons of the rat not only markedly increases, but also becomes qualitatively different when the rats learn a given task, the ratio of the four mononucleotides having changed in forming new combinations.[201-203] The new formed RNA was particularly rich in adenine and uracil. In contrast, in animals which were not subjected to a learning experience, but only to aspecific stimulation of the involved neurons, the RNA content increased, but no variation in nucleotide base composition was noted. In other words, only the cytoplasmic or ribosomic type of RNA (characterized by high values of guanine and cytosine) increased.[202b]

The experimental conditions set up by Hydén *et al.*, in most of their investigations consisted in letting young rats learn to balance themselves on a thin wire inclined at a 45° angle one hour daily for four days or letting right-pawed rats learn to use left paws to get food pills from a glass tube. Individually isolated sensory or motor neurons were analyzed from RNA content.[201a-c] In another type of learning experiment, involving both motor and sensory functions, carried out by Hydén's co-worker, Shashoua,[362] a piece of foam was attached to the jaw of the goldfish so that its head remained above the level of water. In spite of the consequent unusual vertical position of its body, the goldfish soon learned to swim correctly. During this learning process, brain cells synthetized new RNA characterized by high adenine and uracil concentration, RNA which was similar to that synthetized by the trained rats of the experiments described above. No such RNA is produced when the goldfish performs the same amount of swimming but does not learn. Stress, too, does not cause similar RNA change.[201d]

Further experiments by Hydén and Lange[203a] have shown that the composition of nucleotide bases of the new formed RNA in neurons of rats which learned the same type of task described above[202a-c] was DNA-like (high adenine and uracil) a short time after the training, but it changed into the cytoplasmic or ribosomic type (high guanine and cytosine) a longer time after the training. More recently Hydén and Lange[203c] have reported that rats trained on the reversal of handedness show increased protein synthesis in the neurons of the hippocampus as expressed by ^{3}H-leucine concentration. During the establishment of the new behavior (switching to the nonpreferred paw in getting food) an increased incorporation of ^{3}H-leucine occurred in the protein of the hippocampal cells (A₃ region). That the phenomenon is specific for the process and not related only to a sustained neural function has been proved by the fact that it was not observed when training was resumed after thirty days, but it was observed at the resumption of training after fourteen days as well as the fifth day after the initial training. Criticism of the experiments of Hydén *et al.* has been presented by several authors[46, 243] in relationship to the methods used and the interpretations. Adequate discussion of that criticism has been presented recently by Hydén and Lange.

Other experiments by Zemp *et al.*[201-203] somewhat similar to those carried out by Hydén *et al.*,[177-179] but using homogenates of large brain regions rather than of isolated neuronal units, have shown a marked increase of the incorporation of RNA precursors after a fifteen-minute learning experience, such as, for example jumping on a platform to avoid an electric shock. The fact that the increase in RNA incorporation after learning occurred particularly in a region of the brain including the diencephalon may be interpreted by assuming that the phenomenon is related not only to the learning experience, but to other factors, such as the strong emotional reaction (fear) of those animals which could not avoid the shock because of the absence of the platform, and therefore which did not learn. (Additional control was carried out on animals which were resting.) In conclusion, RNA role in learning and memory mechanisms seems to be that of a neurochemical constituent which is produced in a messenger form and which would control protein synthesis within the cell.[147]

In an attempt to establish a comprehensive view of the mechanisms of learning and memory involving both the electrophysiological and biochemical models, Hydén has taken into consideration the glial cells and the mucoproteid material of brain tissue. From the quantitative point of view, in fact, the glial cells have been estimated as numerous as about 90 billion with respect to the estimated 10-12 billion neurons, and the mucopolysaccharide and mucoproteid material of cerebral extracellular space, as forming the 20 per cent of the total brain mass. The morphological and biochemical study of neural tissue in mammals during learning[201b] has suggested that neuronal glia other than a structural material and perhaps a selective barrier between nerve tissue and circulation, also acts in transferring its RNA content into neurons when needed, as during the learning process. Neurons and the surrounding glia seem to form a metabolic and functional unit. [201b, 243, 246] To quote Hydén, who has been the originator of this theory[201b]: "Are the glia more than metabolic appendices to the neuron? Can they also assist the functioning of the neuron by linking together the electrical phenomena and metabolic activities? The experimental evidence, briefly recapitulated below, suggests that they can."

"Certain chemical differences were found between the nerve cells and its glia. The latter contained less RNA and protein but more free lipids. The glia showed high respiratory enzyme activities under moderate functional demands and utilized mainly pyruvate and succinate, whereas the nerve cell principally oxidized glutamate. As a result of stimulation the neuron produces RNA and proteins. This seems to be a characteristic of the neuron as its capacity to produce bioelectrical potentials."

"Metabolically, there is a pronounced symbiosis between the glia and the neuron. The glia possesses a strategic position interposed between the capillaries and the nerve cell. With increasing complexity of the central nervous system in the species the number of glial cells increases relative to that of the neurons.[35*] The highest ratio is seen in man."

"The glia and the nerve cell are energetically linked together in a coupled system, the units of which can swing between two positions. Such a system provides great stability."

"The high respiratory-enzyme activities of the glia at moderate functional demands fell with increasing physiological stimulation,

---

*Quoted by Hydén, loc. cit. 201 b, i.e., Haugh, H., Acta Anat., *19*:60, 153, 239, 1953.

as did the RNA content. In contrast, enzyme activities and production of RNA and protein rose in the neuron, which has high energy demands and utilizes the energy of the electron-transporting system with priority. The glia at the same time partly resorted to anaerobic glycolysis."

"Analysis of the basic composition of the RNA indicated the existence of a coupled mechanism for polynucleotide production in glia and nerve cell. With chemical stimulation, the neuron responded with a prompt synthesis of nuclear (and perhaps cytoplasmic) RNA, the composition of which varied within certain limits. The differences found so far are concerned with guanine and cytosine. Since the composition of the RNA produced can vary according to the type of stimulation, it seems that the proteins produced assist the nervous function. The change in base composition of the glial RNA went in the opposite direction to that of the nerve cell. The glial RNA changes could be observed before those in the nerve cell, and this seems significant. These are metabolic considerations. Are these biochemical processes, involving production of RNA and proteins, linked with the capacity of the neuron to generate bioelectrical potentials in a system serving the nervous function? Although the evidence is far from sufficient, the following may serve as food for thought."

"The nerve impulses contain information in modulated frequencies. The frequency in the neuron is a thousand times higher than in the glia. When increased stimulation effects a change of the frequency in the neuron, that of the glia can be instantaneously changed by a phase looking mechanism. This triggers the release of specific nucleotides in the glia, which are transferred to the neuron. Because their base composition is opposite to that of the neuron with respect to guanine and cytosine, the glia molecules could act as inhibitors of neuronal repressor RNA.[34*] By blocking a repressor RNA in the neuron, enzymes induction and specific protein synthesis could occur to meet the functional demands. The RNA produced in the neuron could partly be used

---

*Quoted by Hydén, loc. cit. 201 b, i.e., Jacobs, F. & Monod, J., J. Mol. Biol., 3:318, 1961.

for synthesis of the enzymes serving the coupled Na and K transport at the membrane."

The recent studies by Adey *et al.*[2] also support Hydén's biochemical theory of learning and memory. These authors have found that sharp changes occur in the electroencephalographic pattern of laboratory animals or human beings during the establishment of a new behavior. By studying the intracellular and extracellular activity of single neurons, they also found that nerve cells generate a primary and a secondary system of electrical waves closely related to the processing of experiential information and that the neuronal electrical activity may be modified by current pathways in the extracellular space.*

Hydén *et al.*[201e] have also carried out an interesting hybridization analysis in the attempt to unfold the biochemical characteristics of the aging neurons. The concept that nerve cells do not usually divide in adult life even though they reform their DNA has been already emphasized. It is well known, on the other hand, that old animals as well as aging human beings learn and consolidate memory very slowly and rather poorly with respect to young beings. The initial results of that investigation have demonstrated that DNA from an old animal may be different from that of a young one. Further experiments have shown that protein synthesis increases at 100 per cent one hour after the injection of prepared brain DNA into the cerebral ventricle of another animal. DNA becomes incorporated in a polymerized state in the brain cells of the recipient animal. Then, through RNA mediation, it stimulates protein synthesis. To quote Hydén

---

*The relationship between the changes in neuronal RNA metabolism and the electrical activity of the involved neurons, especially from the point of view of the quantitation of the increase in RNA production following electrical activity, has been reinvestigated recently by Berry.[36] The study has been carried out on single neuron preparation (the giant neuron of the abdominal ganglion of the marine mollusk *Aplysia californica*), which offers the advantage of allowing precise monitoring of the electrical activity and minimizing the errors due to the production of RNA by nonneuronal elements. The results have shown that the constant rate of incorporation of tritiated uridine into RNA increases under synaptic stimulation and is directly proportional to the number of the action potentials produced by the neuron. Conversely, multineuronal samples from stimulated ganglia failed to show an increase in incorporation.

201d: "A way will be found to add orderliness to brain cells of one individual by incorporation of gene material from another. The most direct would be to infect the brain with genes attached to harmful viruses entering the brain from the mucosa of the nose. All viruses have the capacity of penetrating into host cells, and it should then act as a transporting agent. A necessful counteracting of entropy increases in brain cells could change the whole structure of our societies."

Since Hydén's discovery of the increase of RNA synthesis in brain cells of laboratory animals during learning,[201-203] a great body of research on the biochemical aspects of learning and memory[4, 5, 23-25, 127-129, 172] has been produced along three main channels with the aim to demonstrate suppression of memory by blockage of RNA or protein synthesis, enhancement of memory by stimulation of RNA or protein synthesis, and transfer of memory from learned to naive animals by administration of RNA or RNA brain extracts or crude brain extracts.

Suppression of Memory by Blockage of RNA or Protein Synthesis

The property of several chemicals of the antibiotic family (puromycin, actinomycin-D, acetoxycycloheximide, 8-azaguagine and others) to inhibit protein synthesis has been extensively and successfully utilized in the investigations aimed to prove a cause-effect relationship between protein synthesis inhibition and memory function. The majority of experiments deal with protein synthesis inhibition, since, when the only RNA synthesis was experimentally induced, the animals suffered such widespread and severe disturbances that the issue was grossly beclouded.[358b]

The pioneering experiment carried out by Agranoff and Klinger[5] in 1963 deserves particular description. The goldfish is trained to avoid a shock by swimming back and forth from one component to another across a barrier in the container tank whenever a light flashes so that it recalls the experience for about a month. If the injection of puromycin into the cranial fluid of the unanesthetized fish takes place a few seconds after learning, the goldfish forgets the lesson. If the injection is done within one hour, conversely, it recalls the experience. Interference with the establishment of long-term memory by administration of other protein synthesis inhibitors, such as acetoxycycloheximide,[6] is also resulting from the injection of the inhibitor intracerebrally[24a, b] or subcutaneously.[24c]

The importance of the demonstration that memory consolidation from the trace, just registered, to the permanent memory is prevented by the inhibition of protein synthesis lies in the fact that it throws light on the role of short-term memory as the expression of an electrophysiological event, in the process of definitive storage of information. The classical experiments which demonstrated the obliteration of memory by procedures able to disrupt the continuing electrical activity of the involved neurons (already discussed in Chapter III) have suggested that short-term memory is essential to the establishment of an endurable memory trace. The investigation of Agranoff et al.,[4-6, 88] by showing that the interference with the process of protein synthesis prevents the consolidation of memory, indicates that the initial interpretation reported above is no longer acceptable as correct.

When cytosine arabinoside (ARA-C) is used as an inhibitor of DNA synthesis in goldfish brain, memory of shock avoidance coupled with a light stimulus results as nonaffected.[4] Since puromycin and acetoxycycloheximide block protein synthesis as well as DNA synthesis and they also affect memory consolidation, while cytosine arabinoside does not, even though it inhibits DNA synthesis (by preventing the conversion of cytidine to deoxycytidine), further investigation is needed to clarify the problem. Conflicting data on the effects of protein synthesis inhibitors in rodents, anyway, may be due to overtraining, aversive or convulsive effects of the drug, and even to the holes made by the needles in brain tissue.[4] This should be borne in mind in evaluating the results of those experiments.

Halstead and Rucker,[172] by using tricyanoaminopropene (TCAP),* have shown that the increased rate of the consolidated

---

*The compound 1,1,3-tricyano-2-amino-1-propene (also known as Triap), which is essentially an antithyroid[9, 204] and atoxic antibiotic drug,[201b] has interested students of learning and memory since Egyhazi and Hydén[111] noted in 1961 that

memory parallels the increased concentration in RNA. Since TCAP does not affect RNA formation from DNA, the authors have interpreted long-term memory as partially independent of DNA-produced RNA. RNA synthesis in such a case may be similar to that occurring in RNA viruses which can reproduce inside the host cells without a set of DNA instructions. Halstead and Rucker,[172] therefore, have postulated that consolidated memory may be partially independent of RNA synthesis from DNA and dependent upon the final protein molecule synthetized through messenger-RNA and nonmessenger-RNA. This protein can trigger the original impulse code when the memory must be recalled. In addition to such a task and to that of keeping DNA actively producing messenger-RNA, the protein would have a third role to play, i.e. that of activating messenger-RNA to reproduce itself.

Another significant contribution to the biochemistry of learning and memory has been given over the past few years by J. B. Flexner and L. B. Flexner *et al.*[127-129] in a body of research aimed to clarify the effects of protein synthesis inhibitors on those

---

it stimulates RNA synthesis in single neuronal units. (It also increases the cytochrome oxidase activity in neurons and decreases the RNA concentration in glial cells.[201b]) This effect has been confirmed in further studies, and additional information has been obtained regarding its stimulation of general protein synthesis.[117, 203 a] The property of TCAP as a "learning facilitator" has been described later on by several investigators[68, 86, 117, 351] but not confirmed by others.[55, 167a, 307] A recent study by Davenport[87] has shown that if TCAP is given to immature rats before and after birth at doses sufficient to cause anatomical cretinism (including dwarfism, altered skeletal development, persistence of immature hair and skin feature), an enduring behavorial deficit is produced which is similar to that caused by thyroidectomy in neonatal rats and parallel to the human cretinism due to lack of thyroid hormone. Performance deficits were also noted in rats reared on diets containing TCAP and tested on automatic closed-field maze tests even many weeks after the discontinuation of the drug. Defects were also observed in rats tested while receiving the drug (y-maze reversal and normal close-field maze performance). No difference was noted in the performance deficits of rats treated with TCAP and those treated with thyouracil. In any of the learning situations used, no facilitation of the performance in several tests was detected. These data do not contradict previous observations which favored the facile learning effect of TCAP, observations made in older animals, if one considers the possibility that such facilitation takes place when TCAP is administered in a way to avoid early thyroxine deficiency.[87]

processes. These authors succeeded in showing that memory of a maze learning in mice is blocked by puromycin neutralized by sodium hydroxide injected intracerebrally one or more days after the training experience, and that small intracerebral injections of saline at least up to two months later remove the block and restore memory. Apparently the memory impairment due to the protein synthesis inhibition is not related to the initial process of registration, but rather to that of recall. The interpretation of this mechanism of interference with the expression of memory is that of a reversible interaction of abnormal peptides, such as the peptydil-puromycin, with neuronal membranes, especially the synaptic membrane. The initial experimental testing of this hypothesis is represented by a recent investigation[127b] of the Flexners; the investigation indicated that puromycin hydrochloride neutralized with bases of potassium or lithium, calcium or magnesium, rather than with sodium hydroxide, fails to block the expression of memory of maze learning in mice. The inference is that the failure may be due to cationic binding at anionic membrane sites with the resulting exclusion of sufficient peptydil-puromycin to make it ineffective in blocking memory.[127b]

Further support to those conclusions has been given recently by Mayor's[269] investigation of the effects of puromycin and acetoxycycloheximide on memory in the Japanese quail. Intracerebrally injected puromycin has been shown to cause memory deficit in naive quails trained to discriminate between red and green stimuli. Conversely, puromycin aminonucleoside, acetoxycycloheximide, and saline appear to be ineffective in this respect. Puromycin, too, is ineffective when injected into previously trained birds. Naive quails treated with puromycin perform better than control quails after a single reversal of the visual cues. Difference has been found between high doses of puromycin or acetoxycycloheximide and low doses of puromycin: the former inhibits RNA and protein synthesis; the latter, only protein synthesis. Mayor's interpretation of the mechanism of the inhibition of memory by puromycin is in agreement with that by the Flexners[127-129] in giving importance to the mediation of peptydil-puromycin rather than to the quantitative inhibition of macromolecular synthesis or to some nonspecific action.

Recently Oshima *et al.*[306] have studied long-term olfactory memory in spanning salmon through the electrophysiological measurement of the olfactory bulb activity following intracranial administration of a protein synthesis inhibitor such as puromycin, cycloheximide, and actinomycin-D. The aim was to reconcile the evidence of rapid changes in neuronal RNA, as it occurs in the Mauthner nerve of the goldfish,[337] with the seemingly long-lived, RNA-dependent mechanism of memory function as suggested by the results of the experiments on memory transfer through RNA brain extracts. (See below.) The results of this investigation have shown that the antimetabolites used, especially puromycin, depress the mean recorded magnitude of the olfactory response to home waters and the ability of the olfactory bulb responses to differentially respond to the home versus the nonhome waters,* especially shortly (4-7 hours) after the administration of the protein synthesis inhibitor. Recovery is already well advanced at the nine to twenty-eight hours interval.

Apparently the expression of long-term olfactory memory in homing salmon requires continuous protein or RNA synthesis or both.[306] Because of the restoration (even partial) of memory with one day, it appears that a residual basis for olfactory memory function outlasts the interruption of RNA and protein synthesis. The nature of this residual factor should be ascertained in further studies, but it is already evident that long-term memory is not merely a stamping out of long-lived residual template RNA or protein, but rather a continuous metabolic process. In addition, it appears clear from those experiments as well as from the investigation of Cohen *et al.*,[73] that one of the several protein synthesis inhibitors of the antibiotic family, such as puromycin, interferes with the electrical activity of brain cells, radically modifying the

---

*Homing salmon has been found to be able to distinguish, electrophysiologically, home water from other natural waters (Veda *et al.*, quoted by Oshima *et al.*[306]). The demonstration can be considered as an expression of the long-term memory (in fact, it persists from three to four years) since in that test discrimination always occurs between home water and water in which the salmon has never been.

electroencephalographic pattern in the hippocampus, contrary to cycloheximide which inhibits protein synthesis without any electrophysiological effect on nerve cells. At least puromycin, therefore, may interfere with learning and retention by disrupting the continuous neuroelectric process and not necessarily by inhibiting nucleic acid or protein synthesis in neurons. From this point of view the experiments on suppression of memory by protein synthesis inhibitors have provided evidence that RNA may only serve in transferring information to protein molecules rather than in coding it, and that the messenger-RNA involved in the storage of information must be available before the learning experience.[392c]

Enhancement of Memory

The study of the influence of drugs on learning and memory dates back to 1917 when the psychologist William Lashley[251] noted that the administration of low doses of strychnine sulfate to rats increases the learning rate to run a maze. Only recently, however, a systematic investigation of the effects of central nervous systems stimulants, such as strychnine, picrotoxin, pentylentetrazole, and diazadamantanal, has been carried out after having been established as a criterion of learning the measure of the response latency of the performance by the laboratory animals used, i.e. the time which they take to give the prescribed and measurable test (discrimination task, such as choosing the right pats in a maze to reach a goal, or avoidance response to prevent punishment).[210, 267a, 275, 313, 384]

The initial results concerning the effects on learning of drugs administered just a few minutes before training have shown only a stimulation of alertness, motivation, and muscular coordination, and consequently, an improvement of animal performance on a given task. In further experiments drugs as well as electroconvulsive shock have been administered at intervals directly after the training to establish if they interfered with the consolidation of memory, in which case stimulant drugs may be administered in the interval after the training during which the memory processes are active.

The results of these studies have demonstrated that learning is enhanced by strychnine, picrotoxin, and amphetamine if administered soon after training, but that the effect is absent if drug administration takes place at some maximum time after training, i.e. when the labile period for memory storage is over. Those experiments have also provided evidence of the environmental influences on the learning process. Animals which were maintained in quiet, dark cages at a constant environmental temperature learn better after administration of strychnine, in contrast to those animals which during the same experimental conditions are stimulated with acoustic, visual, or thermic stimuli.

An interesting implication of this research, as far as the mechanisms of memory are concerned, is that the drugs capable of enhancing learning are effective by accelerating the rate at which memory traces are consolidated into permanent memory. It has been experimentally ascertained that the type of forgetting caused by electroshock, which is a typical retrograde type of amnesia (see pages 39, 90-92), may be prevented or attenuated by the administration of stimulant drugs just before or just after training. This problem has been discussed in detail in Chapter III. Regarding strychnine, since its administration cancels the amnesic effect of electroshock, it seems that the previous interpretation that this drug enhances learning by accelerating memory consolidation is no longer tenable.

A more recent investigation[44] has shown that the effects of strychnine and picrotoxin on the rate of acquisition of avoidance behavior in mice are particularly evident when performance at the beginning of the second session is compared with that at the end of the previous session. When nitrous oxide is used immediately after a short training, memory storage becomes impaired. Bovet *et al.*[44] have also noted that the effects of the several centrally acting drugs, such as d-amphetamine, chlorpromazine, and isoniazid, on learning and memory differ from species to species or from strain to strain of laboratory animals. Nicotine (at 0.5 g/kg) facilitates learning an avoidance response in a shuttle-box in two-thirds of mice of one strain (especially if the strain performs at a low level) but has a smaller or negative effect (impairment of performance) in other strains. This effect, however, was noted when arecoline was used. It was also strain-dependent.

Another central nervous system stimulant whose effects on learning and memory have been investigated recently and extensively is magnesium pemoline. In general the results of animal experimentation[116, 149, 156, 325] are more convincing than those obtained in human beings affected by amnesic syndrome of different nature.[58, 300] It has been also shown that brain cells of animals treated with magnesium pemoline contain a high concentration of the enzyme RNA-polymerase.[141, 148] The implication is that the drug enhances the synthesis of RNA. Since the animals whose brain cells were chemically analyzed showed an enhanced retention of a learned aversive behavior, the hypothesis that learning is biochemically characterized by new protein synthesis gets further support.

On the other hand, intravenous administration of RNA in presenile and senile individuals with gross memory impairment, especially of the less remote events, seems to improve the amnesia. The most impressive results have been obtained in arteriosclerotic patients, next in subjects affected by Alzhmeier's or Pick's disease, and least in senile psychoses.[62] These data have been confirmed recently by Odens[300] who treated with magnesium pemoline for years elderly individuals (between 62 and 96) so forgetful that they did not recall even their wives' names. The result was that they became able to retell stories heard one week before and also to concentrate better; they felt and appeared less irritable and tense.

More recently Burns *et al.*[58] have found that the acquisition rate in learning a task in a population of individuals intellectually above the average is not favored by the administration of magnesium pemoline. When doses of 6.25 and 25 mg were used, a learning rate slower than in controls treated with placebo was observed. Similar results were obtained by using dextroamphetamine at the single oral dose of 15 mg. High arousal concentration of the drug interferes with performance and acquisition of complex new associations. In those experiments the subjects (male students) had to learn a reaction time task, i.e. what single key among several randomly assigned ones was the correct response to each light when faced with a row of eight neon lamps and responses keys. A 500-msec interval separated a response and the presentation of the next stimulus. Testing was initiated 2.5 hours after the administration of the drug.

Other pharmacological and chemical agents have been studied in relationship to learning and memory. While oxygen[77] and thyrotoxin[187] have been found to be necessary to the development and maintenance of normal intelligence, alcohol[131, 294] is detrimental, caffeine[294] offers some benefits, such as a temporary improvement of recall, and adenosine seems to improve the consolidation of short-term memory into permanent memory.[267a] Glutamic acid, on the contrary, is ineffective on learning and memory both in man and in laboratory animals.[15, 193]

A more recent study by Osborn *et al.*[305] has shown that the effects of barbiturates (thiopental) on learning and memory are only indirect, i.e. through the general sedative effect and the inherent reduction of the intellectual functioning due to interference with attention, discrimination, and association. No specific evidence was obtained supporting the hypothesis that memory impairment because of barbiturate sedation is due to failure of initial fixation by interruption of the consolidation process, or whether it is due to inability to recall when the physiological state at retrieval differs from that during learning. As far as the effect of barbiturates and tranquilizers on memory retrieval are concerned, see page 34.

Memory function of humans can be affected by lysergic acid diethylamide (LSD 25). This drug causes regressive trends in the recollection of some objects, and a constructing effect on the recall of others has been reported recently by Langs.[248] Schizoid and poorly integrated personalities were found to prevail in subjects who responded to 100 mg of LSD with a regressive alteration of early memories and a shift to a primary mode of experiencing which fosters the recall of memory traces not usually in awareness. Subjects with rather rigid, guarded, inhibited, and obsessive personalities did not experience any early memory alteration after administration of LSD. The double-blind study was carried out by eliciting earliest memories on the pre-test and on the test day with the instruction to disregard the previous recall. Changes found occasionally in the placebo group were not regressive and reflected a search for ready, available, alternate recollections.

Transfer of Memory

The method of transferring experiential information as an investigative approach to the biochemical mechanism of learning and memory developed as an application of the research approach which led to the so-called transforming principle in genetics.[16] In the experiments related to this approach, the DNA of one strain of bacteria was mixed with that of another strain. The result was that the latter became endowed with the genetic characteristics of the donor strain. The implication was that by using RNA, protein, or other substances memory transfer from trained to untrained animals may be achieved.[165]

Memory Transfer in Worms

The American psychologist J. V. McConnell[270a-c] and his co-workers in 1955-56 opened a series of experiments on memory transfer by using flatworms of the Planaria family. Similar investigation was continued by his research team[207, 271, 272, 396] and by other investigators using various laboratory animals and different techniques for the transfer to test the hypothesis that nucleic acids or protein are the carriers of the memory trace.

Following the initial successful attempt by the Dutch investigator P. van Oje in 1920, McConnell first succeeded about three decades later in eliciting a conditioned response consisting in body curling in Planaria receiving a light stimulus paired with an electric shock.[207] The corollary was that the lowest organism to possess bilateral symmetry, a rude form of encephalization and a human synaptic-like nervous system, such as the Planaria, can learn a given task.[207]

Thompson and McConnell[396] focused their attention on the fact that those worms have enormous power of regeneration. They wondered if the regenerated half of a Planaria cut in two would retain the memory trace of the learned experience. McConnell, Jacobson, and Kimble[271] approached experimentally this problem in 1956 by training Planaria at a criterion of twenty-three responses out of twenty-five trials. Then, by cutting them across the middle of the body, the head and tail sections were put in individual bowls and allowed to regenerate within four weeks. The regenerated worms were then retrained to the same criterion, and the scores, calculated with respect to two types of controls, were saved. The interesting, unexpected result was that the tails not only showed as much retention as the heads did, but often did better than the heads by showing no forgetting. Further proof that the cut animal body, not necessarily the part containing the brain, stored the memory trace of learned behavior was represented by the fact that each section of a worm cut into three or more parts showed clear retention of the conditioned response.

It was at this time (1956) that the hypothesis of a chemical change independent of the brain, at least of the worm brain, occurring throughout the Planaria body and being responsible for the learning process and for the storage of the learned experience, was formulated by McConnell and co-workers. The next step in the investigation by those authors was the experiments on so-called cannibalisms. They gave the clear demonstration that learning is transferrable from one worm to another. McConnell, Jacobson, and Humphries[272] conditioned a number of worms, chopped them into small pieces, and hand-fed them to untrained cannibal worms. The result of the experiment, highly significant with respect to that carried out on controls, showed that cannibal worms gave approximately as many conditioned responses during the first days of training as did the cannibals which had fed on the untrained worms.

These results were similar to those obtained by other group of investigators (Corning, Karpick, and John) at the University of Rochester. Corning and John[79] also succeeded in proving that the regenerated Planaria, cut in two halves and regrowing in a medium containing the enzyme ribonuclease (which breaks up RNA), show opposite responses with respect to conditioning saving. In fact, while the heads saved it, the tails did not and showed complete forgetting of the learned experience. The tails could be retrained, but it took about as long the second time as it had the first.

On the basis of Hydén's data concerning the increase of RNA concentration in nerve cells as a result of experience[201b] and of the data reported above, Corning and John gave further support to the hypothesis that learning in flatworms has to be mediated by some molecular change within the organism cells and that such a change may be an alteration of RNA concentration. Gerard's interpretation, according to a personal communication to McConnell, in 1961,[270] was that: "There are probably two distinct but related physiological mechanisms for learning in Planarians. The first such mechanism is the familiar one of neural interconnections which are reshuffled in the brain because of the animal's experience, the so-called circuit diagram model, if I may be permitted the analogy. Structural changes in the neural pathways in the brain would presumably not be altered by ribonuclease, which accounts for the fact that the Rochester head regenerates showed no real forgetting. The second type of memory mechanism, however, involves a change in the coding of the RNA molecules in the cells throughout the worm's body. Presumably, whenever the animals learn, the RNA is altered appropriately so that when regeneration takes place, the altered RNA builds the memory into the regenerated animal right from the start. If the RNA were destroyed by the ribonuclease, it is likely that the DNA in the cells would replace the lost RNA, but this replacement RNA would not carry the changed code since the DNA was presumably unaffected by the learning."

Since the publication of the data of McConnell *et al.*[272] and Corning and John[79] in 1961, the interest of the investigators has been focused on the attempt to extract RNA, DNA, and protein material in general from conditioned Planaria to feed the untrained cannibals. It was hoped to determine the subtle molecular differences between "trained" and "untrained" RNA by proving that RNA causes memory transfer. As a matter of fact, when the total body of trained Planaria is utilized to feed the untrained cannibals, one cannot say which molecule in the food is responsible for the transfer of the memory trace.

RNA Transfer in Other Animals

RNA extracts from the brain of experimental animals different from Planaria (rats and hamsters) have been extensively used by Jacobson.[207] In this approach the bias of the difficulty and sophistication required to train satisfactorily and reliably Planaria seems to be overcome.[31] Another point of debate is the fact evidenced by Hartry *et al.*[177] i.e. that it is necessary only to expose Planaria to light and electric shock before feeding them to other worms to let the cannibal worms learn more quickly the light-shock conditioned response. Perhaps just the extra stimulation represented by feeding and handling the Planaria which were going to be food for the cannibals was necessary and sufficient to favor the conditioning of the latter worms by means of an extraproduction of RNA.

Babich *et al.*[18] conditioned rats and hamsters to the sound of a click or a flash of a light by pressing a lever for a food pill. Once conditioned, the animals were killed and RNA from their brain was injected into the same type of unconditioned animals. The results were that those animals became easy to train, presumably because they had some of the necessary RNA that they would be required to form during learning. The injection worked across species. Rats, in fact, appeared to benefit by injection of RNA obtained from hamsters. Particularly significant is the fact that the untrained rats which received RNA extracts from the trained ones responded to light signals but not to clicks if the extract belonged to animals conditioned to light; they responded to clicks but not to light if RNA extract belonged to animals conditioned to clicks.

Positive results on memory transfer by using RNA brain extracts have been also obtained by Cook *et al.*[76] The authors succeeded in transferring the memory trace of an avoidance conditioned response to a buzzer by an intraperitoneal injection of RNA extracts in rats for fifty-three days. The minimum time required for the RNA injection treatment was three days. When treatment lasted from one-half to four weeks, the results were also positive. The intracisternal administration of RNA extracts from trained to untrained rats for one week has proved to be effective in transferring the learned experience.

Luttges *et al.*,[262] however, failed to cause any transfer of memory in varied experimental conditions in which RNA brain extracts were used.

Memory Transfer Through the Transfer of Brain Homogenates

More consistent results on memory transfer have been obtained when brain homogenates instead of RNA brain extracts of trained laboratory animals were injected by various ways (intraperitoneally, intraspinally, intravenously) into naive animals (rats, mice).[126, 347, 411a-c] Ungar[411a-c] has been able to transfer the memory of a learned task, such as that of being startled by a bell or by an air jet, by injecting intraperitoneally the whole brain homogenate of male rats into albino mice. Specifically, the animals lost as much as half of their startled response within about thirty-six hours, but the control group of rats which were injected with brain homogenates from untrained rats reached the same level of tolerance only after twelve days.

The possibility that brain tissue of trained animals may stimulate learning, even without any conveyance of specific information, was ruled out by experiments in which behavioral changes were attributed only to specific information transferred through brain homogenates. Rats trained to escape an electric shock by running into the left arm of a Y-maze were decapitated when 90 per cent correct response was obtained. Whole brain homogenates were then injected into untrained mice. A control group, formed by mice who were injected with brain homogenates of untrained rats, achieved 90 per cent correct responses only after 297 trials, while the group of mice which received brain homogenates from trained rats needed only 137.5 trials to reach the 90 per cent mark. The implication of these results was that brain homogenates prepared from trained animals contained an encoded information which was transferred into the naive animals and caused the transfer of the memory trace of the learned behavior.

Confirmation of the initial findings has been reported recently by Ungar.[411c] Brain homogenates of thousands of rats, conditioned by electric shock to reverse the natural preference for a darkened cage when offered a choice of dark and lighted enclosures, were injected into mice which naturally prefer the dark. The result was that these mice were converted to a distinct preference for the lit cages. With respect to controls, mice which received brain homogenates from untrained rats spent twice as much time in lighted cages as in darkened ones when given the choice of staying in one or another type of cage.

In other experiments Ungar[411c] has shown that rats, trained to turn right even though their natural inclination was to turn left, had brain homogenates which, when injected into naive animals, caused them to turn right if they were inclined to turn left, and vice versa. This phenomenon has been called "negative transfer of learning." Perhaps the brain extracts carry two conflicting types of information, i.e. anti-bias and directional with the resulting cancellation or predominance of the anti-bias instruction.

An interpretation of this phenomenon by Halstead and Rucker[172] has recently received experimental support. It was hypothesized that two antagonistic effects were operating in relationship to both the type and the quantity of training received. All the rats were trained to choose the lit door in a discrimination box, but the rats in each group received a different number, such as 9, 54, 108, 162, of training trials. A control group received no reward. First to be tested was the recipient preference without reward for the lit or unlit door. Then the recipients were rewarded for the choosing of the darkened door, i.e. the opposite of the training which the donor rats had received. Preference testing before reward showed that recipients of extracts from little trained donors initially preferred the lit door (positive transfer of learning) while rats injected with extracts from overtrained rats initially preferred the darkened door (negative transfer of learning).

These findings suggest that two quantitatively different agents are involved in the transfer process. One comes from early learning, the other from later learning. The fact that no transfer was observed in rats receiving extracts from donors trained to the intermediate level indicates that the two agents are antagonistic in their action. Both negative transfer of learning and the existence of antagonistic agents in early and late learning are difficult to be explained in terms of macromolecular model. Preliminary experiments by Halstead and Rucker suggest that it may be possible to separate the antagonistic agents by chemical procedure. Perhaps a unique biochemical process is involved in negative transfer of learning and in the total process of encoding and retaining information.

More recently Ungar[411c] has demonstrated that the dialysis of brain homogenates removes the active material responsible for the memory transfer and that even a small amount of the dialysate is able to transfer the memory of the learned experience. According to Ungar's report at the 135th Meeting of the American Association for the Advancement of Science (Dallas, Texas, 1968), four memory transfer factors are now in the process of being isolated and purified in his laboratory. They are the following: (a.) association with rat's habituation to sound; (b.) dark-light discrimination in a Y-maze; (c.) dark avoidance; (d.) avoidance of stepping down on a platform. They seem to have a different molecular size or a different susceptibility to inactivation by enzymes (which could mean that they are highly specific). Rather than RNA, they appear to be polypeptides containing from ten to forty amino acids. Perhaps nucleic acids and RNA, in particular, play a significant role in the storage of information. But recall seems more logically related, according to Ungar, to the synthesis of specific protein molecules which are more likely, because of their plasticity, to be chemically manipulated and to circulate in the blood stream.

The results of Ungar's investigation are in line with those of Fjerdingstad,[126] whose experiments were carried out in another laboratory of Baylor University, Houston, Texas. The Danish investigator has also confirmed the phenomenon of negative transfer of learning by using RNA brain extracts rather than whole brain homogenates. He trained for two weeks rats living in a box with two levers to get water only by pressing them alternately. No water was obtained on the second press if pressing occurred twice on the same lever. When crude extracts of brain homogenates from the trained rats were injected intraperitoneally or intraspinally (into the cisterna magna) into the naive ones quartered in boxes where a press on either lever would elicit water, a significant shift to alternate lever pressing occurred in the recipient mice, i.e. a 50 per cent more frequent shift than in a control group of mice injected with brain homogenates from control rats which became experienced in getting a drink as the mice did.

The results of Gurowitz's[167b] investigation on the effects of brain homogenates injections on behavior, on the other hand, fail to support the hypothesis that learning can be transferred using whole brain homogenates. As a matter of fact, none of the rats which received brain material from like-trained, opposite-trained, or untrained animals showed any effect on the learning process (evaluated through operant conditioning in a Skinner box). The metabolic fate of the injected brain material and its systemic effects are still unknown. This information is fundamental to support a chemical basis of the transfer of learning. In this respect Byrne's recent research[62] aimed to prove a mechanism by which an injected substance relocates itself so that it may affect memory is significant. The initial results have shown that the injected tissue of each given organ ends up in the same living organ of the recipient animal, and that the factor responsible for the high localization specificity is thermolabile.

The experimental data discussed above represent, by and large, an adequate basis for considering acceptable the biochemical model of learning and memory based on a macromolecular theory involving nucleic acids. The fact that DNA specifically is rather stable metabolically has as its counterpart the high plasticity of RNA and protein material in general, which is reasonably considered as the "universal effector" of cells. Enzymes, for their part, being proteins and fundamental for the life of cells, have been considered recently as key factors in learning and memory mechanisms not only at the level of synaptic junctions, but also at the level of the neurons themselves.[160, 196, 247] Perhaps the lack of evidence for the existence of any enzyme processes which seem to be required for the specific polynucleotide coding is one of the weakest points of the macromolecular theory of learning and memory based on the role of nucleic acids, whose final expression is presumed to occur through the translation of nucleotide sequences in proteins.

Recently Griffith and Mahler[162] of the Indiana University Chemical Laboratory have developed a more plausible biochemical theory in which memories would be stored in coded form in the DNA of nerve cells (*DNA-ticketing theory of memory*). In order to make such a theory worthy of consideration the authors have first drawn the attention on the current knowledge, making that formulation biochemically reasonable, especially the fact that the nucleotide sequence of DNA molecules may be modified by enzymatic activity, such as methylation of the nucleotide bases, usually cytosine.[164, 220, 249, 367, 378] The modified bases, consequently no longer belong to the primary set of four bases of the nucleotide (guanine, cytosine, adenine, thymine), and therefore, some difficulty arises in the process of recognition of DNA molecules by enzymes or by its ability to combine with control elements such as inducers or repressors. Methylation may affect the rate of protein synthesis by altering the affinity of short operation regions of the DNA long tape-like structure, regions which would be concerned only with the control of the transcription or translation of the information.

The DNA-ticketing theory of memory as hypothesized by Griffith and Mahler requires a mechanism for the control of protein synthesis. The experiments on slime moulds[389] have suggested that at 5′-end of a messenger-RNA there are a number of repeating groups of nucleotides, each one called a "ticket," which serve a control function rather than coding the amino acids. One of those tickets is chopped off each time a ribosome passes along the messenger-RNA, and after all tickets have been removed, the messenger-RNA becomes degraded, or the ribosome subunits no longer attach. The number of tickets in the messenger-RNA is equal to the number of protein molecules synthesized per each messenger-RNA, and since the messenger tickets are transcribed from DNA tickets, the number of protein molecules to be synthetized during the lifetime of the messenger is equal to the number of DNA tickets adjacent to the initiator of the appropriate cistron.

The ticketing hypothesis of the DNA theory of memory would provide, according to the above-named authors, an intriguing way to ascertain the number of times a neuron has fired in the lifetime, if one accepts that the simplest way to consider the memory function as a biochemical phenomenon is to suppose that at each neuron firing the restoration of the membrane potential is associated with the synthesis of the fixed quantity of some compound X. In the case that an extra ticket is added to the DNA at any neuron firing, no tickets being present at the beginning, then the total number of times the neuron has fired would equal the total number of tickets and the total number of protein molecules synthetized for each corresponding messenger-RNA molecule. By assuming that a given cistron concerned with the memory function has a fixed, genetically determined number of tickets adjacent to it, that an unmethylated ticket (T) is transcribed, and a methylated one (Tm, or masked ticket) is not; and also by assuming that at the beginning of life all tickets are methylated and that each time a neuron fires a methylated ticket gets unmasked, one could see how after x firings each messenger-RNA molecule is issued with x tickets and produces therefore x protein molecules before being degraded. The system becomes saturated when x equals the number of genetically determined tickets adjacent to the cistron.

By considering the DNA-ticketing theory of memory with respect to the function of synapses and particularly to the modification of their strength during the simultaneous firing of two contiguous neurons, one might expect that a rather large number of tickets would be needed to achieve the synaptic modification. But this seems to be improbable. One may speculate, however, that synapses tend spontaneously to revert back to some standard strength, and that in such a case, if the strength is proportional to the number of tickets on a particular cistron, this number might execute a random walk, i.e. up on each joint firing and down on each spontaneous alteration. The spontaneous movements would represent a sort of forgetting.

Another hypothesis which may be considered in the attempt to overcome the difficulty mentioned above is to think that the neurons involved in memory may have a relatively high threshold so that the average time per second that two contiguous neurons fire simultaneously becomes much smaller.

As far as the process of the initial laydown of the memory trace is concerned, as seen through the mechanism of the passage of macromolecular material through the synaptic membrane following the simultaneous firing of neurons and as seen in the frame of reference of the DNA-ticketing theory of memory, an interesting speculation is that the transported material is an enzyme (or cofactor) which is expected to modify a ticket, precisely by methylation or demethylation. By ignoring the configuration of the two methylated or two nonmethylated tickets, and conversely, by recognizing the configuration of one methylated and one nonmethylated tickets, or vice versa, and perhaps the configurations of a methylated ticket-cistron and nonmethylated ticket-cistron, the enzyme material which would be transported across a synapse would be ultimately degraded and might last only long enough, on each occasion, to demethylate or methylate one ticket. One realization of this model would be if the postsynaptic cell could maintain on its soma and dendritic processes a number of terminal boutons from the presynaptic cell proportional to the concentration of a critical protein produced by its own ticket messenger. The number of boutons generated might even be equal to the number of tickets. Then after each joint firing, a new bouton would appear in the fullness of time.[162]

The DNA-ticketing theory of memory deserves further attention and experimental validation since there is evidence that the methylation process is a determinant in the specific destruction of foreign DNA,[282] that neuronal DNA does not appear to be capable of some form of limited turnover,[161] and that the ribosomes contain an endonuclease which might qualify as the ticket-removing enzyme.[343] The experimental testing of that theory may follow different pathways of attack, for example, by showing that memory disturbance is associated with lack of the essential amino acid methionine (the methyl group required for the methylation process of the ticket should be provided by methionine), or by demonstrating a systematic alteration with age in the number of methylated bases or their dependence upon degree of stimulation or severity of learning programs in laboratory animals. As far as the possible magnitude of the problem is concerned, one should keep in mind that the chemical modification per neuron or synaptic junction during a learning experiment is extremely small, possibly in the range of a few hundreds of transmethylations of nucleotide bases per second throughout the whole brain in order to obtain sufficient information storage per second.[335]

One further argument in favor of the biochemical model of learning and memory, in the sense of the storage of the experiential information in code form in the nucleic acids of the nerve cells, especially synthetized for this purpose, is that it would account for the extremely high capacity of storage of information within the 10-12 billion neurons (10^{16}-10^{20} bits),[296] which is certainly exceeding the usual needs expressed by a still high figure, i.e. 10^{11} bits equivalent to the acquisition of about 30 bits a second continuously for a hundred years.[12, 335] Another interesting estimation, in this respect, is that within the minimal lapse of time of one tenth of a second, which according to some perception tests represents a single "frame" of experience to which a human being may be exposed, the brain may make an impression of thousands of bits of information. The brain, consequently, during the average of seventy years of life of a human being may receive and store in the waking state about 15 trillion information units, i.e. an amount of information one hundredfold greater than the total number of neurons which it contains.[144a]

In the case of an RNA molecule, formed by a chain of four distinct nucleotide bases, each link can be one of the four which one can call A, B, C, and D. By considering a two-link chain, any of the $4 \times 4 = 16$ different combinations may be expected, i.e. AA, AB, AC, AD, or BA, BB, BC, BD, or CA, CB, CC, CD, or DA, DB, DC, DD. By considering a three-link chain, any of the

4 x 4 x 4 = 64 combinations may be expected, and so on. In the hypothesized case that an RNA molecule is formed by twenty-five links, instead of by hundreds as it really is, it has been estimated that one could have any of a million billion different combinations of RNA molecules. This would still be the same original RNA and able to file away every necessary bit of information. The possibility that neurons form RNA molecules at random response to an experiential information and that, therefore, an RNA molecule is formed that has already been formed on other occasions in response to a different sensation seems to be very unrealistic because of the very high number of combinations which make practically equal to zero the chance of accidental duplication.[14]

Another interesting and promising biochemical approach to the study of the mechanism by which the brain selects and organizes the flood of information that is constantly received is that which a team of investigators under the direction of Dr. R. Grenell and Dr. E. Romero[159] took since 1962 at the neurobiology laboratory, University of Maryland School of Medicine, Baltimore, Maryland. By using the perfusion technique the researchers have investigated the electrical response of a selected area of the cat brain (5 mm in diameter) after the replacement of blood by fluids whose constituents are known and can be altered at will. The cortical area, in other words, becomes under complete chemical control. The results of this study have been presented at the annual meeting of the American Association for the Advancement of Science, Boston, 1969.

The investigation of Dr. Grenell *et al.* represents the expansion of the research designed and carried out since about one decade ago by the Swedish neurophysiologist Holger Hydén, based on the testable assumption that the synthesis on new specific protein material triggered in a chain reaction by the increase in concentration of DNA and RNA in brain cells, as a consequence of stimulation, constitutes the biochemical (macromolecular) basis of learning and memory mechanisms. (See page 95.) The assumption formulated by the American investigators was that whenever a signal stimulates a brain cell, something may happen not only at the level of the nucleic acids contained in the cell, but also at the level of the surface layer of neurons, i.e. specifically an alteration of the ion movement across the nerve cell membrane.

The first problem to be tested was the possible change of the new RNA produced during the cell stimulation by altering the normal concentration of ions on either side of the membrane. Because of the fundamental role of sodium and sodium pump mechanism in the functioning of neurons as electrical transmitters, sodium was the first ion to be experimentally altered at the level of cell membrane. All sodium was taken out of the normal perfusion fluid and replaced by choline (a substance needed for acethylcholine synthesis). This does not change the osmolality of the perfusion fluid (a modified Krebs' solution containing potassium, magnesium, calcium, phosphate, bicarbonate, glucose, and protein in the form of a special gelatine), but it causes an accumulation of the choline in the cell since there is no choline pump. The expected result was the absence of the evoked response by a stimulus such as a flashlight or a sound occurring twelve minutes from the beginning of the perfusion. About forty-five minutes were necessary for the recovery of the response from the suppression of the perfusion. By gradually reducing the amount of choline to the point that the substance replaced only the 25 per cent of the original sodium in the perfusate, the time necessary to cover the response was delayed, and that for recovery shortened.

The next experiment consisted of adding the cardiac glycoside ouabain to the perfusate containing 75 per cent sodium and 25 per cent choline, but in a small concentration, i.e. two micromoles, so that no poisonous effect on the nerve cells was noted (because of the changes in the molecular structure of the membrane due to the suppression of the sodium pump and prevention of ATP-ase operation in the membrane). Conversely, a heightened or facilitated response occurred. This unpredicted response was interpreted as resulting from the fact that ouabain affected the molecular structure of the cell membrane in such a way that choline got in and became bound to the receptors to which acethylcholine had been bound. Consequently acetylcholine was released and the inhibitors which normally subdue or prevent the response were inhibited.

To test the hypothesis that choline was essential for the facilitated response, the acetylcholine antagonist, i.e. atropine, at the concentration of 20 millionth of a gram, was added to the perfusate containing ouabain and choline. The facilitated response was suppressed, and it reappeared when the perfusate containing ouabain and choline was made free from atropine. The implication was that something which was not cholinergic became cholinergic at the level of the nerve cell membrane through the appropriate molecular manipulation at that level. Since the neurohormone acetylcholine, considered as fundamental as a chemical mediator of nerve cell functioning, can be turned on when ordinarily is off, speculation has arisen that a neuron is not always one functional entity or another and that under specific conditions different temporary pathways can be opened up for the transmission of incoming information.

Of course, the inferences drawn by those experiments are valuable more as a model for brain functioning, such as that in which the poison ouabain—not present in the brain—was used, rather than for the brain itself. But if in the investigation attention is given to the part of the central nervous system which has been shown to be able to facilitate a cortical response, such as the arousal system called reticular core, then by providing in this way a sort of modulated frequency input, one could still consider the experimental model described above as a good representative of a natural physiological situation in the brain. The experimental testing of this hypothesis has been successful since the stimulation of the reticular core about 30 msec before recording the electrical activity following adequate stimulation of the optic tract in the cat produced a facilitated response similar to that elicited in the ouabain-choline model, a response remarkably higher than that resulting from the stimulation of the optic tract alone. The addition of atropine to the perfusate blocked completely the facilitated response.

Grenell and Romero's interpretation is that the turning on or off of the acethylcholine system of brain cells may occur spontaneously in the cortex as resulting from the prior arrival of an input from the reticular core. The fact noted by Hodgkin that a huge infusion of calcium into the axon of the squid occurred after the perfusion of the nerve cell with virtually the same concentration of ouabain and choline that Grenell and Romero used in their experiments has suggested to these authors that the triggering factor of the acethylcholine release may be a modification of calcium concentration inside and outside the nerve cell.[159]

The facilitated response described above was noted again when a perfusion fluid with 50 per cent of the normal calcium concentration was used, and it was blocked again when atropine was added to the perfusate. By changing the calcium concentration in different directions, the electrical-cortical response appeared facilitated when calcium was higher inside the cell and blocked when it was higher outside the cell. The role of calcium, in other words, may be that of a cation needed inside the cell in a concentration higher than on the outside in order to assure the turning on of the acethylcholine "switch," i.e. the inhibition of the acethylcholine binding and its release, with the final effect of enhancing the cortical electrical response.

Calcium seems also important to maintain the RNA concentration in the nerve cell. Grenell and Romero,[159] in fact, have noted a drop of RNA concentration in neurons when the calcium level in the perfusion fluid reached high or low levels. This has been interpreted as representative of the extremely delicate role of calcium ions for the proper functioning of brain cells, especially as far as the relationship calcium-RNA and in turn RNA and learning and memory functions are concerned. The clinical counterpart of this concept is that patients with gross alteration of calcium metabolism show impairment of intellectual functions, memory included, and that those functions improve significantly when the serum calcium of those patients returns to physiological levels.

By extrapolating the results of Grenell and Romero's investigation from the level of the cell to that of the entire organism and its behavioral acts, one can see how important is the observation of the relationship between the facilitated response and the microchemical environment of the nerve cells. By studying the latter during the establishment of a conditioned response in a laboratory animal, the authors have thrown light on the chemistry of this process and made inferences on the biological foundation of the biochemical mechanism of thinking. After perfusing atropine into the sensorimotor cortex of animals in which a conditioned response was already established, they noted that, while the unconditioned response is unaffected, the conditioned one is completely blocked, presumably because the acethylcholine "switch" turned off and the temporary connection established between given neurons (according to the current interpretation of the mechanism of the conditioned response) became blocked by the antagonist of acethylcholine, i.e. atropine. The switching mechanism is the establishment of a temporary connection in Grenell and Romero's hypothesis. As a matter of fact, they succeeded in showing that the conditioned response abolished by atropine is reestablished by perfusing the cortical tissue with atropine-free perfusate. Since the conditioned response is one of the various examples of learning, it is justifiable to share Grenell and Romero's view that ". . . the brain functions in essence because there exists a series of switches which allow adaptational responses to be made by the brain. The brain can adapt, it must adapt to the various inputs it receives from both the outside and the inside." "All these . . . inputs come in, and one way or another the brain has got to continuously switch off and switch on. The acethylcholine-induced inhibition of inhibition is one means by which the brain does it." ". . . it is a system very similar to the switches that operates in semiconductors, certainly one of the characteristics of its functioning is that of not being expensive in the sense that only those impulses fitting the specific relationship with the input signals, the nerve cell membrane and the presynaptic ending will be allowed to pass through a particular neuronal network." "The number of possible permutations is practically unlimited and each network has its own unmistakable identity."

The investigation of Grenell *et al.* also appears to be an improvement of the experimental approach to the study of brain functioning with respect to older approaches which interfered with the input signals and therefore with the operation of the "switches." It deserves, consequently, attention and consideration for further development.

Chapter IV

DISCUSSION OF A UNIFYING CONCEPT OF LEARNING AND MEMORY:

NEUROPHYSIOLOGICAL MECHANISM (ELECTROCHEMICAL MODEL)

In an attempt to establish some meaningful correlations between electrophysiological and biochemical mechanisms of learning and memory, it should be borne in mind that a fundamental difference exists between true molecular coding of experiential information and the specificity manifested in molecular recognition. To quote the neurophysiologist F. O. Schmitt[358b]: "In true *molecular coding*, codons (e.g., the nucleotide bases of DNA and RNA), through specific sequential array in a system capable of replicating the sequence and of reading out specific portions by forming messenger-RNA, process the encoded information in a biologically meaningful way. The codon sequences are like the block index in a library; for each card there is a book with its stored information available for retrieval. Such systems are conveniently dubbed coding of the 'library type.' Molecular recognition is manifested when clusters of aminoacids in proteins, as active sites, match the structure of substrate molecules, hence exert their catalytic influence. Another example is the correspondence in structure between antigen and its specific antibody."* "This type of molec-

---

*This concept has been the core of an interesting model of learning and memory as seen at the cellular level and which involves the biochemical processes of molecular rearrangement of nucleic acids and proteins, i.e. the *biochemical-immunological model of learning and memory*. The underlying theory is that the emergence of a protein with a conformation formerly not peculiar to the organism would represent the structural (macromolecular) modification occurring during and after the learning experience and responsible for the storage of that experience in the form of memory and for its recall when needed. Immunologically speaking, the newly emerged information can be described as a new antigenic structure for the particular protein surface.[279] The structure of an antigenic determinant or arranged recurring bonds, such as peptide bonds, perpendicular to which as a whole determine the specificity of the particular determinant, is translated into the language

ular recognition or 'memory' as applied to the brain processing of information, discussed recently by Eigen,[113] is most likely to manifest itself by selectively determining the connectivity of neurons with each other at synaptic junctions to form specifically 'wired' nets. One variant of the specific molecular recognition theory portrays specific proteins and antiproteins as 'synaptic solder' in determining which of many possible circuits will fire in processing an 'engram'."

The "library type" of coding assured by codon sequences is an alternative or variant of the synaptic "solder type" of coding according to which specific molecular recognition will depend upon the attachment at the synaptic level of specific proteins or antiproteins with resulting different possibilities. One group of electrical circuits rather than another will fire and, therefore, process the engram.

Confronted with the evidence coming from several types of investigations on the biochemical mechanisms of learning and memory, the "library coding model," i.e. "one idea-one engrammatic molecule" corresponding to the genetic "one protein-one gene" concept, does not appear as convincing and realistic as the "synaptic soldering type" of model, in which the neuronal circuit specification, rather than molecular recognition, would depend upon the synaptic soldering between neurons. Lashley's accepted concept, that the narrowly deterministic explanation of learning and memory mechanisms based on the pure electrical model is inconsistent with the evidence of plasticity of brain functioning and the related behavior, should not be interpreted, as

---

of a nucleotide sequence. The final expression of the memory coded in the nucleic acids of the nerve cells would be through the translation of nucleotide sequences into amino acid sequences and finally in proteins. Since information in nature is transmitted not only in the direction of DNA to RNA and to proteins, but also vice versa, the mode in which antibodies are formed in the organism from the various fragments of peptide chains remains still not described on the basis of the biochemical-immunological model of learning and memory. The DNA of the organism would provide most of the material of the antibody molecules whose active side is essentially formed by the antigen. Essential to that model is the presence of a barrier between brain and blood. Obviously the passage into the circulation of the new antigens on the neuronal surface during the disintegration of the membrane would cause auto-immune disorders.

Hydén[201d] has pointed out, in the sense that: "brain cells contain mechanistically taped 'memory molecules' that store information. This is a biological nonsense."

Conversely, one may look at the problem in a way in which the chemical substances of the donor's learned brain can be recognized as the material which facilitates specific as well as non-specific stimulus-response patterns in the naive brain of the recipient. In other words, in the electrical model of learning and memory, the role of the signal would be that of forming a new tangible structure. The biochemical or macromolecular model would give to the signal the significance of a means simply to select the information which has been formed and incorporated in the brain tissue as nucleic acid or protein in general.

A more comprehensive hypothesis would be one which considers the signal as fixed to an appropriate receptor and transmitted from neuron to neuron by a chemical mediator. If the establishment of on-off combinations of neuronal units in the form of patterns is essentially an electrical event, in which an important part for the formation of the pattern is played by the permeability of the synaptic membrane (electrochemical event), the molecular recognition between neurons, perhaps a sort of refinement of the mode in which each cell of the body recognizes the others, seems fundamental for the recognition of the peripheral and central connections of each of the 10 million neuronal pathways of labeled lines among the 10-12 billion neurons.

A bit of information may be recognized as such by the recognition of the neuronal pathway of that map through which the electrical impulses travel, recognition which is made possible by the distinctive chemical trait of each nerve fiber. This process presides over the embryonal development of the nervous system and may account for the mechanism by which learned information is converted and recorded into molecular structure.

The electrical and biochemical events may integrate each other when one considers that the newly synthetized protein formed during learning and accounting for memory storage may constitute an electrogenic material responding to electrical fields of brain tissue; it may also undergo conformational changes, activate chemical transmitters, alter the physico-chemical state of synapses, and be incorporated in the cell membrane in a stable configuration.[358b] The potential role that molecules might play in the transformation processing in the nervous system has been conceived as being similar to that of paracrystalline structures. Protein, DNA, RNA, and other molecules have properties analogous to those of the dynamic structures represented by the crystal mesophases. Liquid crystals, in fact, may order spontaneously their interchangeable smetic or nematic phase, orienting in electric and magnetic fields, into specific tridimensional configurations, and they may respond to mechanical, thermic, electrical, and chemical stimulations.[330e]

The intercellular space of brain tissue is filled with hyaluronic acid fibers, ions, and proteins packed together into approximately 150 Å tubular structures. Hydration of hyaluronic acid and molecules may affect ion movement by filling or organizing the intercellular space. Differential movement of metabolites and gene products along the microtubules and around filaments may contribute to the role that molecules seem to play in the mechanism of information processing. Learning experience would provide the bridge between prelabeled but still unconnected pathways connecting peripheral and central neuronal units. The simultaneous firing of the prewired neurons to be connected would elicit the exchange and combinations of molecular labels and would establish the connection. Learning would result from this synchronous activity of neurons belonging to different pathways. Since the control of the molecular structure of the labeled lines of the neural pathways along which the impulse travels seems to be genetically determined, it appears possible that the labeling process goes farther in the nervous system and becomes responsible for the synaptic connections between neurons which have the same label.

In John's hypothesis,[215] learning and memory processes and brain functioning as well represent neurophysiologically temporal and spatial patterns of billions neurons and glial cells. Each neuronal unit and its surrounding glia interact electrochemically with each other and with the neighboring neurons and glial cells in a pattern form. Neuronal activity patterns change in relationship to experience and account for the behavior inherent to that experience. Learning and memory are both dynamic and static processes. The continuing activity of neurons represented by the passage of the electrical impulse through neuronal units interconnected in patterns would account for short-term and intermediate memory. The permanent memory storage would result from some static residues of that continuing activity and from some structural alteration of physical, chemical, and electrochemical nature at the level of synaptic junctions with the effect that these neuronal connections would become facilitated in allowing the electrical impulses to travel around the patterned groups of neurons.

In John's terminology, an experiential stimulation would alter the baseline activity of the population of neurons. The temporal sequence of states of the neuronal network is called "mode" of activity. The increase in probability of coherent activity in that "mode" constitutes the stored memory. Information storage consists of increasing the likelihood that a particular "mode" of coherent oscillation will be produced in the neuronal network from some period of time. The sequence of events would be the following: (a.) A new experience is perceived. The stimulus causes an alteration of the neuronal network from some period of time. It initiates a reverberating electrical signal among a set of neurons. As the short time signal leaps across, a thousand chemical processes become activated at the synaptic junctions; (b.) The alteration of the neuronal network induces RNA synthesis or even the construction of proteins or polypeptides. The protein material forms a longer lasting but still temporary memory trace; (c.) In hours or days anatomic changes take place in neurons so that these become the soldered wiring of long-term memory. Proteins maintain the synthetic cycle and modify the responsiveness of cell membranes to particular sequences of stimulation. Thus, the chemical changes occurring during memory consolidation increase the probability of the "modes" of oscillation originally caused by the stimulus event.

Memory retrieval would require a mechanism that assesses the congruence between the oscillation of cells which display invariant responses to afferent stimulation ("stable cells") and the oscillation of cells whose coherence has been influenced by prior experience ("plastic cells"). Initiation of the oscillation of the plastic cells would constitute retrieval and the coincidence between the two "modes" would indicate that the event is familiar.

John, however, appears still vague concerning the mechanism by which the retrieval of experiential information results in initiation of action, i.e. in excitation of the effector controlling performance relevant to the recalled information. An interesting hypothesis, in this respect, is that which Pribram *et al.*[330e] have formulated recently on the basis of an extensive investigation on visual reception, which was already discussed in Chapter II in relation to the problem of memory localization. By testing a visual discrimination task in monkeys, they succeeded in demonstrating that the visual information which the animal perceived did not represent a pure and simple coding of light patterns focused on the retina, but rather the effect of their integration with information already linked to a learned response. The input is modified before reaching the specific sensory areas of the cerebral cortex inherent to that given stimulus, and finally it becomes distributed over a widespread portion of the cortex.

The mode in which this distribution takes place has been hypothesized as similar to the optical artifact characterizing the tridimensional picture obtained by lensless photography called "hologram."[252]* Such a physical event may also account for the

---

*The method of "wavefront reconstruction" or *holography* was developed about two decades ago by Dr. Dennis Gabor of C.B.S. Laboratories, Connecticut. When in 1960 the laser beam became available, the hologram appeared not only applicable to projection but also able to give an account for a possible mechanism by which the input signals representing experiential information become distributed throughout the surface of the cerebral cortex. When a beam of coherent light is split so that a "reference" part of the beam interacts with a portion of the beam reflected from an object, a complex interference or diffraction pattern takes place, and it spreads over entirely on a photographic plate. The object is recorded in the form of such interference, and since the pattern is widely distributed on the

real nature of the memory trace, being able to satisfy the known electrophysiological requirements of brain functioning and being capable of experimental verification. The notion of a temporo-spatial representation, as the dispersing variable in a distributed holographic model of the nervous system, has been introduced.

As a matter of fact, the hologram provides an explanation of the capability of the brain to store an enormous amount of information in a rather limited space. (See page 123.) One can fit even 10^5 bits of information in one plane of the film and accommodate even 10^{12} information units by considering all planes available. In addition, since the hologram can reproduce an entire image by using just a piece of the original image in the reference wave, which means that it allows output of an entire information set by using any point of entry, one can explain another feature of the brain, such as its capability of using many different points of entry to retrieve a specific item of information. Any point of the hologram may be active as the site of information pertaining to different objects depending upon the storage of physical alterations at that point in the film induced by the reference wave and also depending upon its response to a particular reference wave in conjunction with all the points surrounding it. An individual point may be used as an active part or carrier of any different information sets. Multiple information on the same film by using the same points may be obtained by changing an object into an object beam and by changing the reference angle beam. Likewise in brain functioning it appears necessary for a single neuron to be a member of various specific information sets of neurons in order to assure the storage of a great amount of information.

Further, the hologram hypothesis may account for the ability of the brain to use both temporal and spatial referents for recalling information. As a matter of fact, the hologram, too, can be made by using a temporal or spatial reference. That a temporal ordering characterizes the process of memory scanning seems to

film, it appears meaningless until coherent light illuminates it. Then the disassembled parts of the original image become assembled again and the form of the object reappears.

be possible since a strong temporal relation has been observed in recovery from memory loss due to trauma.[406]

Finally, the Markovian factor or the distributing feature inherent in the mathematics of both phenomena seems to be another factor of analogy between brain and hologram principle of functioning. As far as visual function is concerned and also as support to the concept that an interference effect may operate in the central nervous system functioning, Rodieck[346] has shown that it is possible to describe mathematically by convolution integrals the initiating events between the stimulation of a retinal receptor and the operation of a neuronal unit located nearby. From the standpoint of its shape, a close analogy exists between the visual receptive field of a single retinal neuron and a convolution of a derivative of the shape of the retinal image obtained at that point. On the other hand, the role of the coherent light source necessary to make and display the hologram may be represented, as far as the general brain functioning and the optic function specifically are concerned, by the parallel arrangement of thousands of connections between the retina and the visual cortex, or by the rhythmic firing of the nerve cells of the optic neuronal chain, and last but not least, by the numerous and varied detectors responding with great sensitivity to even extremely small stimuli such as a tilt of a line.[191]

One can understand the mode in which the interference effect is produced in the brain tissue so that the hologram hypothesis of memory storage and retrieval may be verified. With Pribram[330e] one can imagine that "when nerve impulses arrive at synapses they cause electrical events on the other side of synapses which take the form of momentary standing wave fronts. The patterns set up by arriving nerve impulses presumably make a microstructure of wave forms that can interact with similar microstructures arising in overlapping junctional contacts. Then other microstructures are derived from the spontaneous changes of the electrical potential that ceaselessly occur in nerve tissue and from other sources within the brain. Immediate across correlations result and these can add to produce new patterns of nerve impulses." It may be conceivable that the totality of this process has a more or less lasting effect on protein molecules and perhaps other macromolecules at the synaptic junctions, and can serve as a neural hologram from which, given an appropriate input, an image can be reconstructed. The hypothesis formulated by Pribram seems to fit the requirement that "the information is distributed throughout the stored hologram and is thus resistant to insult."[330e]

The mechanism of recall is the result of an organizing process involving both the anterior (frontal) and posterior association cortex (temporo-parietal cortex surrounded by the various primary sensory areas). Such an organizing process consists essentially of transformations within the input channels before the incoming signals reach the specific primary sensory areas. Transformations must take place within a stable framework to be effective as codes. The stored microstructures of the synapses, the parallel pathways of the input system, the specific detector sensitivities of the units in the systems, the redundancy of the external environment, and for new and complex information, the concomitant functioning of the associative areas of the cerebral cortex, and the interconnections between them and several subcortical structures may represent the stable framework within which the input transformation would take place.[330e]

The hologram model of the process of remembering is not objection-free. For example, it appears difficult to compare the fluid milieu of the brain and the hologram. The latter differs essentially from the former since it requires fixed geometric positions. However, in a recent review of the Longuet-Higgins model, which is an extension of the hologram techniques from light to sound (phono-holograms), it has been emphasized that the exact geometry of the optical hologram is not a fundamental requirement, since many methods of storage and recovery of information about both amplitude and phase (or their counterparts) might serve in analogous situations. [39] It has been also pointed out that the high technical precision required in the construction and the retrieval of a hologram contrasts to the limits of the technical prevision operating in the constraints of brain structure.

Chapter V

SYNTHESIS

This monograph opens with a discussion of the impressive revival during the past decade of the study of brain functioning at the light of some spectacular and significant technological advances, such as those which occurred in electronics, cybernetics, and computer design and applications. This is not to mention the impact that they had upon the neurophysiological approach to the most specific manifestations of brain functioning and to those aspects of that functioning which fall under the domain of psychiatry, psychology, behavioral sciences, and philosophy. Perhaps none of the brain functions has focused the attention of neuroscientists over the past ten years as much as learning and memory have. There is no question that these processes are the most essential of the total brain functioning.

The mode in which the impression of information takes place and the ways by which it becomes definitely fixated as a long-term memory trace in the brain has been partially clarified on the ground of an electrophysiological model. Still partially unfolded, however, appears today the mechanism of recall of the stored information. Interesting and promising seems to be the biochemical or macromolecular approach which has been developing since the middle fifties when chemical techniques have attempted to uncover the mysteries of chromosomes. This trend of research has suggested that memory traces are permanently stored in the form of new protein molecules. They may interfere with synaptic function, so allowing a unifying modality of action which accounts for the electrophysiological and biochemical phenomena occurring within the neuronal units.

Learning and memory processes are defined from the psychological and neurophysiological viewpoints. After having given a definition of intelligence as well, this mental function is discussed in relation to memory function, to clinical methods of testing it, and to the problem of techniques of teaching and methods of education.

The various types of learning, such as by association, trial and error, observation and insight, maladaptive, motor, and rule learning, as well as the part played by repetition in learning and the phenomena of habituation and dishabituation, and decrement and extinction are also discussed. Emphasis is given to the contribution of "Gestalt" psychologists and behaviorists from one side and more neurophysiologically-oriented students on the other side in the attempt to clarify the mechanisms of those processes.

It has been pointed out that even though no experimental demonstration has ever been given to the hypothesis of the existence of specific nerve pathways from the periphery of the brain centers in support to the Watsonian-Pavlovian concept of learning and memory by association, the concept of conditioning, however, is still valid, and within this context a detailed description of the various types of conditioned responses, from the classical ones to the operant and the instrumental types, is offered. The classical conditioning involves involuntary acts controlled by the autonomic nervous system. Operant and instrumental conditioning involve voluntary muscular responses controlled by the central nervous system. By appropriate use of the instrumental conditioning, learning to control vegetative functions and therefore psychosomatic symptoms appears possible. The critical implications are that one type rather than different types of learning exist, that central and autonomic nervous systems are physiologically equipotential, and that there is no reason to differentiate the hysterical type of psychiatric symptoms from the psychosomatic ones, as far as the nature of their origin and the ways to control them are concerned. Emphasis is also given to the significant part that learning and repeated training play in the process of thought formation. Rather than innate ability, thinking is the end result of long lasting learning. In this process the role of language is fundamental.

Learning development, as resulting essentially from Piaget's basic contribution, is also discussed with particular emphasis on the social and educational implications of the modes and ways human beings learn during the various phases of their physical and mental development.

As far as the memory function is concerned, the three phases of registration, retention, and recall are discussed, and the psychological mechanisms and factors underlying them (decay, interference, facilitation, divergent, and convergent productions, mediators, cues, strategies) are analyzed.

Trace-model and dual-trace-model of memory are then outlined and the role of recognition and transfer recall in the phase of retrieval discussed. Mention is made of the role of consciousness in learning and memory functions and the implications of this concept in psychoanalytic theory and practice discussed. Forgetting, at this point, is evaluated as an automatic versus an act of will. Repression, suppression, and catharsis through abreaction are then discussed in the frame of reference of memory function. Organic versus psychogenic amnesias are then analyzed.

* * *

As far as the *influence of heredity and environmental factors on learning and memory* is concerned, the experimental evidence that behavioral patterns are hereditary is presented. Genetic factors influence both the speed of the conditioning process producing a given behavior in laboratory animals and the nature of the inherent mechanisms of memory storage. Learning is better achieved when practice periods are spaced.

Concerning the influence of the environment on learning behavior, particularly significant is the fact that animals which grew up in a sensory enriched environment, especially those of the young age group, are more capable of solving problems, such as getting through a maze, and that the neurons of their brains appear larger and richer of protein and enzymes and better supplied of blood. The environmental impoverishment seems to cause the most impressive changes in the morphological and biochemical makeup of brain tissue, in the direction opposite to that of the sensory enriched environment. Also significant is the fact that modification of the preweaning environment affects the emotional more than the adaptive type of behavior.

As far as nutritional factors are concerned, there is evidence that malnutrition interferes with learning and memory functions during the growth of animals and humans both during the fetal and neonatal life. Malnutrition after birth is only partially responsible for the impairment of those functions as well as those of the inherent behavioral deviations and of the respective physical changes. Prenatal nutritional deprivation reduces cellular growth of the brain to the point that irreversible damage occurs even though strong corrective efforts are made subsequently. This is also true for any other organ, but the brain seems to be the most sensitive and certainly the unique organ which, if damaged, may affect man's ability to improve his life and that of other men with whom he is in social contact.

The earlier in life malnutrition occurs, the more profound and permanent is the impairment of the ability to learn and memorize. The degree of malnutrition, however, remains to be determined. What is for sure is that the effects of malnutrition are less severe and reversible if they interfere with growth during the phase of cell enlargement, more severe and irreversible if they interfere with growth during the phase of cell proliferation. Preliminary studies in humans suggest that the effects of malnutrition on brain functioning duplicate those demonstrated in laboratory animals. Time is an essential factor. If in early life severe malnutrition occurs, brain growth is affected, and it is manifested by lesser circumference and weight as well as by reduced concentration in protein and nucleic acids and of DNA polymerase activity. If malnutrition is more proteic than caloric in the sense of deficit, permanent retardation in developing learning behavior and sluggish responses to various environmental stimuli occur. If it is more caloric than proteic, those behavioral changes still take place, but the solving ability is generally preserved.

In human beings the first three years of life are crucial as far as the influence of malnutrition on learning and behavior is concerned. Early weaning and the absence of a substitute for human milk is the usual cause of infantile marasma. Late weaning (2-3 years) and lack of food supplement, with the inherent protein deficiency, are responsible for Kwashiorkor. Regarding the effects of maternal starvation during pregnancy on fetal growth, it has been shown that the prematurity rate remains unchanged. There is no doubt, however, that the risk of abnormal fetal nutrition and growth is higher in infants whose mothers were malnourished during pregnancy. Psychological, cultural, and socioeconomic factors are responsible for intellectual development, but the role of nutrition is the most important. About 300 million children suffer of varying degrees of malnutrition, and those of underdeveloped countries score consistently low on intelligence tests. When malnutrition and infection interact with each other, malnutrition favoring infection and infection making possible the clinical onset and the rapid deterioration of the symptoms of malnutrition, the total effect is greater than the sum of the single effects. Therefore, prevention and therapeutic action should be directed toward both factors by providing more and better food (food more rich in protein) and adequate vaccines and medication.

* * *

Regarding the problem of *learning and memory localization* in the brain, evidence is presented in support of the concept that specific memories are not located in specific regions of the brain. Even though the temporo-parietal portion of the cerebral hemispheres appears to be the most probable site where integrative phenomena occur to assure fast and effective retrieval, and even though a particular structure of the cerebral nervous system may be involved in the mediation of a certain behavior (but its absence would not be a necessary condition for the elimination of that behavior), it seems that memory traces are made by entrance into the function of patterns of neuronal units which are widely represented throughout the cerebral cortex of both hemispheres. They are interconnected with each other and with some subcortical structures, especially those of the reticulo-limbic system, which also contribute to the emotional color with which the memory traces are reexperienced during the recall.

The role of the cerebral cortex remains that of a sophisticated representation center accounting for refinement, magnification, and redundancy of the sensory input. Since the initiation of the neuronal network firing at times causes inhibition of nearby neurons, it seems more accurate to think in terms of a floating-point notion rather than of a specific neuronanatomical space when considering the neuronal net with respect to general brain functioning and to learning and memory processes specifically.

*   *   *

In the section of the monograph devoted to the *biological mechanisms of learning and memory* (neurophysiological models: electrophysiological and biochemical or macromolecular), the available material is critically discussed with the twofold aim to clarify the interaction of the electrophysiological and biochemical events in an attempt to understand better the mechanisms of registration, permanent fixation and retrieval of experiential information, and the general mechanics of brain functioning as well.

The electrophysiological model, which originates from Hebb's "semiautonomous cell assemblies theory," is critically discussed also by analogy between the brain electrophysiological functioning and the functioning of the electronic computer machines. There is evidence for considering learning and memory as processes resulting from an electrophysiological mechanism consisting of temporal and spatial patterning of neuronal circuits in which a static change (physical and/or electrochemical) is left behind the passage of the impulse, most probably at the level of synapses. The formation of functional contacts between axons reaching a given gnostic field and the integration of particular stimuli patterns to the point that they become recognized any time they are presented would account for the perceptual type of learning. The associative type of learning would consist of the establishment of functional synaptic connections between units of different gnostic fields representing particular stimuli, if these coincide in time, or—as an alternate hypothesis—of the convergence of messages originating from the neurons that represent each of the paired stimuli onto plurimodal associative neuronal units.[208b]

The demonstration that brain functioning is not only conductive in type in the sense that the main goal is the propagation of the electrical impulses from neuron to neuron, but also retentive because of the structural and functional (electrophysiological) alteration of the synapses and primarily because of the macromolecular change occurring in the brain cells during and after learning, has been the most significant achievement of brain research in the last decade. Initiated with the discovery that the RNA content of neurons increases during learning, the biochemical approach to the study of learning and memory has progressed through different routes, all directed to prove that the new synthetized material (not necessarily nucleic acid) is responsible for the permanent storage of information and of its retrieval. In one research trend the hypothesis that memory, if consisting of a molecular event inherent to the information of a new protein material, can be transferred from trained to nontrained animals by administration of brain extracts or RNA or RNA obtained from brain extracts has been successfully tested. Present evidence points to peptides more than to any other material as responsible for memory transfer in laboratory animals. Some experimental data, however, are controversial, and further investigation is required to establish the metabolic fate of the injected brain homogenates as well as their systemic effect in the recipient animals.

In another experimental approach, memory enhancement by administration of RNA or chemicals which increase RNA or protein synthesis in the brain cells of laboratory animals or human beings with memory deficits has been investigated. The results are very uncertain, however, and less promising in humans than in laboratory animals.

In a third type of experimental approach to the study of learning and memory biological mechanisms, the effect on those functions of chemicals which inhibit proteins synthesis have been studied. The results appear partially successful and still under debate also because one of the most commonly used protein synthesis inhibitors, such as puromycin, seems to interfere with learning and memory processes not only through a direct macro-molecular effect at neuronal level, but also through the altera-tion of the electrical activity of the nerve cells.

The total body of research discussed in previous paragraphs by and large appears to be an adequate foundation for the macro-molecular model of learning and memory. A more plausible bio-chemical theory, able to account for the mode in which memory is stored in coded form in the DNA of nerve cells, emphasizes the experimentally proved existence of enzymatic processes for modifying the nucleotide sequence of DNA, which chiefly involve the methylation of bases, usually cytosine. As a matter of fact, one of the weak points of the DNA theory of learning and mem-ory seems to be the lack of evidence of any enzyme processes required for the translation of the nucleotide sequences into amino acid sequences and finally into proteins.

After a detailed discussion of this theory, which is called DNA-ticketing theory of learning and memory, attention has been di-rected onto another biochemical trend of brain research aimed specifically at the clarification of how the brain selects and or-ganizes the flood of information that is constantly received and what happens chemically in the brain cells during a classical Pavlovian conditioning. A small cortical area is maintained under strict chemical control through the proper perfusion technique, and the molecular changes (essentially ionic) occurring at the level of the nerve cell membrane are then analyzed. This ap-proach offers the advantage of not interfering with the input signals in the experimental procedure. The initial results are en-couraging in indicating that the brain functions essentially by turning on or off a series of "switches," similar to those operating in semiconductors, which allow adaptational responses to various external and internal inputs.

The mode in which the integration of the *electrophysiological model* of learning and memory—which accounts more specifically for the initial phase of registration of information—with the *bio-chemical model*—which accounts better for the permanent storage and recall of information—takes place is discussed critically in the last section of this monograph taking into consideration the experimental data as well as the most promising hypotheses which have been inspired by them. The synthesis of a new protein material at the level of synapses or within the neurons themselves and its electrogenic property allowing it to respond to electrical fields of brain tissue, undergo conformational changes, activate chemical transmitters, alter the physicochemical state of synapses, and be incorporated into the cell membrane in a sort of stable configuration may account for both the transient and definitive fixation of the memory trace. Rather than the "library type" of coding in which information seems to be assured by codon sequences of nucleic acids, the synaptic "solder type" of coding appears to be more probable. Specific macromolecular recognition will depend upon the attachment at the synaptic level of specific protein or anti-protein material with the result that one rather than another neuronal circuit will fire and process the engram. How the engrammatically stored information is psychophysiologically scanned and retrieved and in what way the macromolecular structure carrying the information becomes an actual activity pattern in efferent pathways, i.e. how brain functioning is coupled with performance and behavior in general, is still under scrutiny. The solution of these problems represents the basic goal of further research on learning and memory. Interesting and promising theories are discussed.

* * *

As far as the *mechanism of general brain functioning* is concerned, in light of the data accumulated over the past decade, especially those concerning learning and memory processes, the brain no longer appears to be a passive receiver and transmitter of information, but rather a biological system actively functioning in a fashion analogous to that of electronic computer machines. If in the inut-output functioning of a computer the predictability is a basic characteristic, that is only partially true for brain functioning. The uncertainty of brain functioning, a condition deriving from the stochastic nature of neuronal operation, i.e. of firing at random spontaneously so causing a "noisy" background in the system whose average expression is an unimportant aspect of neuron behavior and does not tell when its parameters are psychologically significant in determining a given behavior of other neurons, is also supported by the well-established fact that different types of learning or development may result in different types of nerve-net combinations.

The general mechanics of the central nervous system seems to be characterized, at least on the basis of the data concerning the mammalian visual systems which are the most complete, by the spontaneous, automatic, and selective firing of neurons in a patterned fashion. The firing of a single neuron in the neuronal network is not followed by firing throughout the entire net. The initiation of the firing of the neuronal network, therefore, requires some type of summation effects because of the multiple firing by several neurons. A simple stimulus, in other words, may cause the firing of many redundant neurons. It has been also shown, that an effective stimulus causes a maximal difference between the firing rates of adjacent neurons with the result that some become excited; others, inhibited. When the maximal disturbance of the neuronal units is limited to the smallest number of neurons in the presence of sensory stimuli, the brain response remains stable. Finally, it has been shown that the brain is able to modify the input signals before they reach the specific sensory areas where they are destined, so that eventually the incoming signals become widely distributed throughout the cerebral cortex.

The mechanism of the distribution, storage, and retrieval of the memory trace has been hypothesized as being similar to interference patterns of laser-produced "holograms." In that optical artifact which is called "hologram" the information, for example, that of a scene, is recorded in a photographic plate in the form of a complex interference or diffraction pattern, which, when illuminated by coherent light, reforms the original image. The hypothesis is interesting because remembering or recollecting literally implies a reconstructive process, i.e. the assembly of dismembered mnemonic events. It would involve the associative areas of the cerebral cortex (anterior or frontal regions and posterior regions located between the various primary sensory areas) and consist essentially of transformations (coding operations) within the input channels before the incoming signals reach the specific sensory areas of the cortex.

The stable framework of the coding operations would be provided by the stored microstructure of the postsynaptic events, by the parallel pathways of the input system, by the specific detector sensitivities of the units in the system. It would be provided, especially for new and complex information, by the concomitant functioning of the associative areas of the cerebral cortex with the contribution of some subcortical structures of the brain, such as the reticular core, the amygdala, and the hypothalamic nuclei.

If those concepts about learning and memory mechanisms and general brain mechanics will be confirmed as correct, one may be tempted to consider that many types, rather than just one unique, universal mode of thinking, exist, each one individually molded during the physical and psychological development of the individual. A true objective appreciation of the environment seems hardly to be obtainable according to this view, which is in sharp contrast with the three-century-old cartesian concept of an objective understanding of the world. However, the conclusions drawn from the studies of the mammalian visual system appear to unfold better not only the problem of learning and memory mechanisms, but also that of the development of the central nervous system.

Even though it is still speculative if the lasting changes occurring in certain cortical neurons are an essential component of the learning process, it is an accepted fact that conditioning procedures can produce those neuronal changes. Analogously, it is a well-established fact that nonuse of certain apparently preestablished central nerve pathways leads to their nonfunctioning as well as to a failure in development of certain central nerve connections. Further understanding of the mechanisms of learning and memory processes and brain functioning in general, therefore, may be predicted as resulting not only from additional investigation of brain mechanics, but also from the study of the effects of the environmental stimuli on the brain structure and functional operations.

BIBLIOGRAPHY

1. Adams, J. A.: *Human Memory.* New York, McGraw-Hill, 1967.
2. Adey, W. R., Kado, R. T., and Walter, D. O.: Impedal Characteristics of Cortical and Subcortical Structures: Evaluation of Regional Specificity and Hypothermia. *Exper. Neurol., 11:*190-216, 1965.
3. Adrian, E. D.: *The Physical Background of Perception.* Oxford, Clarendon Press, 1947.
4. Agranoff, B. W.: Memory and Molecules. *Psychiat. Spect., 5:*7, 1968.
5. Agranoff, B. W. and Klinger, P. D.: Puromycin Effect on Memory Fixation in the Goldfish. *Science, 146:*952, 953, 1964.
6. Agranoff, B. W., Davis, R. E., and Brink, J. J.: Chemical Studies on Memory Fixation in the Goldfish. *Brain Res., 1:*303-309, 1966.
6a. Agranoff, B. W., Davis, R. E., Casola, L., and Lim, R.: Actinomycin D Blocks Formation of Memory of Shock Avoidance in Goldfish. *Science, 158:*1600, 1601, 1967.
7. Akelaitis, A. J.: A Study of Gnosis, Praxis and Language Following Section of the Corpus Callosum and Anterior Commissure. *J. Neurosurg., 1:*94-101, 1944.
8. Albert, D. J.: a) The Effect of Spreading Depression on the Consolidation of Learning. *Neuropsychol., 4:*49-64, 1966; b) The Effects of Polarizing Currents on the Consolidation of Learning. *Neuropsychol., 4:*65-77, 1966; c) Memory in Mammals: Evidence for a System Involving Nuclear Ribonucleic Acid. *Neuropsychol., 4:*79-92, 1966.
9. Allen, J. R., Lalich, J. J., and Schmidt, M. J.: Effects of 1,1,3-tricyano-2-amino-1-propene on the Thyroid and Testes of the Rat. *Lab. Invest., 14:*1412-1418, 1965.
10. Allison, R. S.: *The Senile Brain.* London, Arnold, 1962.
11. Alpert, D. and Bitzer, D. L.: Advances in Computer-Based Education. *Science, 167:*1582-1590, 1970.
12. Anderson, A. R.: *Minds and Machines.* Englewood Cliffs, N. J., Prentice-Hall, 1964.
13. Andreassi, J. L. and Whalens, P. M.: Some Physiologic Correlates of Learning and Overlearning. *Phychophysiol., 3:*406-413, 1967.
13a. Ashby, W. R.: Contribution of Information Theory to Pathologic Mechanisms in Psychiatry. *Brit. J. Psychiat., 114:*1485-1498, 1968.
14. Asimov, I.: *The Human Brain.* New York, Houghton Mifflin, 1964.
15. Austin, A. W. and Ross, S.: Glutamic Acid and Human Intelligence. *Psychol. Bull., 57:*429-434, 1960.

16. Avery, O. T., MacLeod, C. M., and McCarty, M.: Studies on the Chemical Nature of Substances Inducing Transformations on Pneumococcal Types: Induction of Transformation by Deoxyribonucleic Acid Fraction Isolated from Pnemococcus Type III. *J. Exper. Med.*, 79:137-158, 1944.

17. Avis, H. H. and Carlton, P. L.: Retrograde Amnesia Produced by Hippocampal Spreading Depression. *Science*, 161:73-75, 1968.

18. Babich, F. R., Jacobson, A. L., and Bubach, S.: Cross Species Transfer of Learning: Effects of Ribonucleic Acid from Hamster on Rat Behavior. *Proc. Nat. Acad. Sci. U.S.A.*, 54:1299-1302, 1965.

19. Barbizet, J.: Lobe Frontale et Mémoire. *Ann. Medico-Psychol.*, 2:289-302, 1965.

20. Barlow, F.: *Mental Prodigies.* London, Hutchinson's Scientific and Technical Publications, 1951.

21. Barnes, R. H., Cunnold, S. R., Zimmerman, R. R., Simmons, H., McLeod, R. B., and Krook, L.: Influence of Nutritional Deprivation in Early Life on Learning Behavior of Rats as Measured by Performance in a Water Maze. *J. Nutr.*, 89:399-410, 1966.

22. Barnett, S. A.: *The Rat: A Study in Behavior.* London, McGibbon & Kee, 1967.

23. Barondes, S. H.: Relationship of Biological Regulatory Mechanisms to Learning. *Nature*, 205:18-21, 1965.

24. Barondes, S. H. and Cohen, H. D.: a) Puromycin Effects on Successive Phases of Memory Storage. *Science*, 151:594, 595, 1966; b) Delayed and Sustained Effect of Acetoxycycloheximide on Memory in Mice. *Proc. Nat. Acad. Sci. U.S.A.*, 58:157-164, 1967; c) Memory Impairment After Interacerebral Injection of Acetoxycycloheximide. *Science*, 160:526-527, 1968; d) Arousal and Conversion of "Short-Term" to "Long-Term" Memory. *Proc. Nat. Acad. Sci. U.S.A.*, 61:923-929, 1968.

25. Barondes, S. H. and Jarvik, M. E.: The Influence of Actinomycin on Brain RNA Synthesis and on Memory. *J. Neurochem.*, 11:187-195, 1964.

26. Bartlett, J. C.: *Remembering.* Cambridge, Cambridge University Press, 1932.

27. Beach, F. A. and Jaynes, J.: Effects of Early Experience Upon the Behavior of Animals. *Psychol. Bull.*, 51:239-263, 1954.

28. Beach, F. A., Hebb, D. O., Morgan, C. T., and Nissen, H.: *The Neuropsychology of Lashley.* New York, McGraw-Hill, 1960.

29. Bechterev von, V. M., *General Principles of Human Reflexology.* International, 1932.

30. Behrend, E. R., Powers, A. S., and Bitterman, M. E.: Interference and Forgetting in the Bird and Fish. *Science*, 167:389, 390, 1970.

31. Bennet, E. L. and Calvin, M.: Failure to Train Planarians Reliably. *Neurosc. Res. Progr. Bull.*, 2:3-24, 1964.

32. Bennet, E. L., Rosenzweig, M. R., and Diamond, M. C.: Rat Brain Effects of Environmental Enrichment and Wet and Dry Weights. *Science,* 163:825, 826, 1969.
33. Bennet, E. L., Diamond, M. C., Krech, D., and Rosenzweig, M. R.: Chemical and Anatomical Plasticity of Brain. *Science, 146:*610-619, 1964.
34. Bental, E. and Bihari, B.: Evoked Activity of Single Neurons in Sensory Association Cortex of the Cat. *J. Neurophysiol., 26:*207-214, 1963.
35. Berlucchi, G.: Rapporti fra Formazione Reticolare del Tronco dell'-Encefalo e Attivita' Nervose Superiori. *Acta Neurol., 23:*1022-1032, 1968.
36. Berry, R. W.: Ribonucleic Acid Metabolism of a Single Neuron: Correlation with Electrical Activity. *Science, 166:*1021-1023, 1969.
37. Bettinger, L. A., Davis, J. L., Meickle, M. B., Birch, H., Kopp, R., Smith, H. C., and Thompson, R. F.: "Novelty" Cells in Association Cortex of the Cat. *Psychonom. Sci., 9:*421, 422, 1967.
38. Bianchi, L.: Contributo alla Dottrina delle Afasie. *Ann. di Neurol., 24:* 237, 1906.
39. Bigelow, J. H.: Proc. Fifth Conference on Information and Control Processes in Living Systems. Pacific Palisades, California, February 23-26, 1969.
40. Bishop, M. P., Elder, S. T., and Heat, R. C.: Intracranial Self-Stimulation in Man. *Science, 140:*394, 396, 1963.
41. Bitterman, M. E.: Toward a Comparative Psychology of Learning. *Amer. Psychol., 15:*704-712, 1960.
42. Blakemore, C. B. and Falconer, M. A.: Long-Term Effect of Anterior Temporal Lobectomy on Certain Cognitive Functions. *J. Neurol. Neurosurg. Psychiat., 30:*364-367, 1967.
43. Bogoch, S.: *The Biochemistry of Memory.* New York, Oxford University Press, 1968.
44. Bovet, D., Bovet-Nitti, F., and Oliverio, A.: Genetic Aspects of Learning and Memory in Mice. *Science, 163:*139-149, 1969.
45. Bovet-Nitti, F., Oliverio, A., and Bovet, D.: Effects of Cross-Fostering on Avoidance Learning and Freezing Behavior of DBA 25 and C 3 H/He Inbred Mice. *Life Sci., 7:*791-798, 1968.
46. Bowman, R. E. and Harding, G.: Protein Synthesis During Learning. *Science, 164:*199-200, 1969.
47. Braun, J. R. (Ed.): *Contemporary Research on Learning.* New York, Van Nostrand, 1963.
48. Brazier, M. A.: *The Electrical Activity of the Nervous System.* New York, Macmillan, 1961.
49. Briggs, M. H. and Kitto, C. B.: The Molecular Basis of Memory and Learning. *Psychol. Rev., 69:*537-541, 1962.

50. Brill, H. *et al.* (Eds.): *Neuropharmacologia.* Amsterdam, Excerpta Medica Foundation, 1967.
51. Broadbent, D. E.: Short-Term Memory. *New Scientist, 16:*2-21, 1962.
52. Bronowski, J. and Bellugi, U.: Language, Name and Concept. *Science, 168:*669-673, 1970.
52a. Brown, M. H. and Lighthill, J. A.: Selective Anterior Cingulotomy: A Psychosurgical Evaluation. *J. Neurosurg., 29:*513-519, 1968.
53. Brown, R. Z.: *Ecol. Monogr., 23:*257, 1953; quoted by Bovet, D. *et al.* (Ref. 44).
54. Brudner, H. J.: Computer-Managed Instruction. *Science, 162:*970-976, 1968; 54a. Bruner, J.: Quoted by Elkind, D. (Ref. 114).
55. Brush, F. R., Davenport, J. W., and Polidora, V. J.: *Psychonom. Sci., 11:*95, 1968; quoted by Davenport, J. W. (Ref. 87).
56. Buresova, O.: quoted in *Med. World News, 10:*5, 1969.
57. Burns, B. D.: a) *The Mammalian Cerebral Cortex.* London, Arnold, 1958; b) *The Uncertain Nervous System.* Baltimore, Williams and Wilkins, 1969.
58. Burns, J. T., House, R. F., Fensh, F. C., and Miller, J. G.: Effects of Magnesium Pemoline and Dextroamphetamine on Human Learning. *Science, 155:*849, 851, 1967.
59. Buscaino, G. A.: a) Perche' Sognianmo. Sull'Importanza dei Movimenti Rapidi Oculari per il Contenuto Visuo-Motorio dei Sogni. *Acta Neurol., 20:*373-400, 1965; b) Considerations on the Importance of Rapid Eye Movements on Visual Dreams. *Acta Neurol., 23:*847, 852, 1968.
60. Buscaino, V. M.: a) *Biologia della Vita Emotiva.* Bologna, Zanichelli, 1921; b) *Neurobiologia delle Percezioni.* Napoli, Ed. Sc. Ital., 1946; c) La Meccanica del Cervello. *Rass. Med. Sarda, 9-10,* 1953; d) Fondaments Neurologiques des Phenomenes de Conscience. *Acta Med. Belg.,* 1957, and *Acta Neurol., 13:*93, 1958; f) Vita Psichica e Attivita' Cerebrale. *Acta Neurol., 15:*277, 1960; g) Sempre in Tema di "Vita Psichica e Attivita' Cerebrale." *Acta Neurol., 4:*432, 1961; h) Udito e Linguaggio dal Punto di Vista Neurologico. *Acta Neurol., 18:*133, 148, 1963; i) Brain and Conscious Experience. *Acta Neurol., 22:*153, 1967; j) Abstract of the paper of Retif, J. *et al. Acta Neurol., 22:*903, 1967. (Ref. 339).
61. Byrne, W. L. (Ed.): *Molecular Approaches to Learning and Memory.* New York, Academic Press, 1970.
62. Byrne, D. and Worchel, P. (Eds.): *Personality Change.* New York, Wiley, 1964.
63. Cabak, V. and Najdanvic, R.: *Arch. Dis. Child, 40:*532, 1965; quoted by Eichenwald and Fry, see No. 112.
64. Cameron, D. E., Solyom, E. L., Sved, S., and Wainbrib, B.: Effects of Intravenous Administration of Ribonucleic Acid upon Failure of Memory for Recent Events in Presenile and Aged Individuals. In Wortis, J.(Ed.): *Recent Advances in Biological Psychiatry.* New York, Plenum, 1963.

65. Campbell, B. A. and Church, R. M. (Eds.): *Punishment and Aversive Behavior*. New York, Appleton-Century-Crofts, 1969.
66. Castellucci, V., Pinsker, V., Kupfermann, J., and Kandel, E. R.: Neuronal Mechanisms of Habituation and Dishabituation of the Gill-Withdrawal Reflex in *Aplysia*. *Science, 167*:1745-1748, 1970.
67. Cerletti, U.: L'Elettroshock. *Riv. Sper Freniatr., 64*:310, 1940.
68. Chamberlain, T. J., Rothschild, G. H., and Gerard, R. W.: Drugs Affecting RNA and Learning. *Proc. Nat. Acad. Sci. U.S.A., 49*:918-924, 1963.
69. Chorover, S. L., and Schiller, P. H.: a) Short-Term Retrograde Amnesia in Rats. *J. Comp. Physiol. Psychol., 59*:73-78, 1965; b) Re-examination of Prolonged Retrograde Amnesia in One Trial Learning. *J. Comp. Physiol. Psychol., 61*:36-41, 1966.
70. Chesler, P.: Maternal Influence in Learning by Observation in Kittens. *Science, 166*:901-903, 1969.
71. Christensen, P. R.: *The Functioning Sharing Approach in Research on Joint Man-Machine Intelligence*. Santa Monica, System Development Co., 1963.
72. Cohen, H. D. and Barondes, S. H.: Puromycin Effect on Memory May be Due to Occult Seizures. *Science, 157*:333, 334, 1967.
73. Cohen, H. D., Barondes, S. H., and Ervin, F. R.: Puromycin and Cycloheximide: Different Effects on Hippocampal Electrical Activity. *Science, 154*:1557, 1558, 1966.
74. Colley, W. W. and Glaser, R.: The Computer and Individualized Instruction. *Science, 166*:374-382, 1969.
75. Collins, R. L.: Inheritance of Avoidance Conditioning in Mice: A Diallel Study. *Science, 143*:1188-1190, 1964.
76. Cook, L., Davidson, A. B., Davis, D. I., Green, H., and Fellows, E. J.: Ribonucleic Acid Effect on Conditioned Behavior in Rats. *Science, 141*: 267-269, 1963.
77. Corah, N. L., James, A. C., Painter, P., Stern, J., and Thuston, D.: Effects of Perinatal Anoxia After Several Years. *Psychol. Monogr.* 79:No. 3, 1965.
78. Corning, W. C. and Balaban, M. W.: *The Mind, Biological Approaches to its Function*. New York, Wiley, 1968.
79. Corning, W. C. and John, E. R.: Effect of Ribonuclease on Retention of Conditioned Response in Regenerated Planarians. *Science, 134*:1363-1365, 1961.
80. Cowley, J. J. and Criesel, R. D.: The Development of Second-Generation Low Protein Rats. *J. Genet. Psychol., 103*:233-242, 1963.
81. Cravioto, J., Delicardie, E. R., and Birch, H. G.: Nutrition, Growth and Neurointegrative Development: An Experimental and Ecologic Study. *Pediatrics, 28*:319-372, 1966.

82. Cronholm, B. and Blomquist, C.: Memory Disturbances after Electroconvulsive Therapy. 2. Conditions One Week after a Series of Treatments. *Acta Psychiat. Neurol. Scand.*, *34*:18-25, 1959.

83. Cronholm, B. and Molander, L.: a) Memory Disturbance after Electroconvulsive Therapy. I. Conditions Six Hours after Electric Shock Treatment. *Acta Psychiat. Neurol. Scand.*, *32*:280-306, 1957; b) Memory Disturbance after Electroconvulsive Therapy. 5. Conditions One Month after a Series of Treatments. *Acta Psychiat. Neurol. Scand.*, *40*:211-216, 1964.

84. Cronholm, B. and Oltoson, J. O.: Ultrabrief Stimulus Technique in Electroconvulsive Therapy. *J. Nerv. Ment. Dis.*, *137*:117-123, 1963.

85. Crowcroft, P. and Rowe, F. P.: Social Organization and Territorial Behavior in the Wild House Mouse (*Mus Muculus L.*). *Proc. Zool. Sci.*, *140*: 517-551, 1963.

86. Daniels, D.: The Effect of TCAP on Acquisition of Discrimination Learning in The Rat. *Psychonom. Sci.*, *7*:5, 6, 1967.

87. Davenport, J. W.: Cretinism in Rats. Enduring Behavorial Deficits Induced by Tricyanoaminopropene. *Science*, *167*:1007-1009, 1970.

88. Davis, R. E. and Agranoff, B. W.: Stages of Memory Formation in Goldfish: Evidence for an Environmental Trigger. *Proc. Nat. Acad. Sci. U.S.A.* *55*:555-559, 1966.

89. Dawson, R. G. and McGaugh, J. L.: Electroconvulsive Shock Effects on a Reactivated Memory Trace: Further Examination. *Science*, *166*:525-527, 1969.

90. Delafresnaye, J. P. (Ed.): *Brain Mechanisms and Learning*. Springfield, Thomas, 1961.

91. Delboeuf, J. L. R.: *Théorie Génerale de la Sensibilité*. Bruxelles, 1876.

91a. Delgado, J. M. R.: *Physical Control of the Mind*. New York, Harper & Row, 1969.

92. Denenberg, V. H. and Karas, G. G.: Interactive Effects of Age and Duration of Infantile Experience on Adult Learning. *Psychol. Rep.*, *7*:313-322, 1960.

93. Denenberg, V. H., Ottinger, D. R., and Stephens, M. W.: Effects of Maternal Factors Upon Growth and Behavior of the Rat. *Child Develop.*, *33*:65-71, 1962.

94. DeSilva, C. C.: Common Nutritional Disorder of Childhood in the Tropics. *Adv. Pediatr.*, *13*:213-264, 1964.

95. Deutsch, J. A.: The Physiological Basis of Memory. *Ann. Rev. Psychol.*, *20*:85-104, 1969.

96. Deutsch, J. A. and Deutsch, D.: *Physiological Psychology*. Homewood, Ill., Dorsey, 1966.

97. DeValois, R. L.: Color Vision Mechanisms in the Monkey. *J. Genet. Physiol.*, *43*:Suppl. 2, 115-128, 1960.

98. Dewson, J. H.: quoted by Pribram. (Ref. 330e).

99. Diamond, M. C.: Extensive Cortical Depth Measurements and Neuron Size Increases in the Cortex of Environmentally Enriched Rats. *J. Comp. Neurol., 131:*357-364, 1967.
100. Diamond, L. T. and Hall, W. C.: Evolution of Neocortex. *Science, 164:* 251-262, 1969.
101. Dingman, W. and Sporn, M. B.: Molecular Theories of Memory. *Science, 144:*26-29, 1964.
102. Dinsdale, H. B.: Proc. Ann. Meeting, Royal College of Physicians and Surgeons of Canada, Montreal, Canada, 1969.
103. Dixon, T. R. and Horton, D. L. (Eds.): *Verbal Behavior and General Behavior Theory.* Englewood Cliffs, N. J., Prentice-Hall, 1968.
104. Dollard, J. and Miller, N. E.: *Personality and Psychotherapy.* New York, McGraw-Hill, 1950.
105. Drachman, D. A. and Arbit, J.: Memory and the Hippocampal Complex. II. Memory is a Multiple Process? *Arch. Neurol., 15:*52-61, 1966.
106. Duncan, C. P.: The Retroactive Effect of Electroshock on Learning. *J. Comp. Physiol. Psychol., 42:*32-44, 1949.
107. Ebbinghaus, H.: a) *Über das Gedachtnis.* Lypsie, Druncker, 1885. b) *Memory. A Contribution to Experimental Psychology.* New York, Columbia University Press, 1913.
108. Eccles, J. C.: a) *The Neurophysiological Basis of Mind. The Principles of Neurophysiology.* Oxford, Clarendon Press, 1953; b) The Physiology of Imagination. *Sci. Amer., 199:*135-142, 1958; c) *The Physiology of Synapses.* New York, Academic Press, 1964; d) (Ed.) *Brain and Conscious Experience.* Berlin, Springer-Verlag, 1966.
109. Edström, A.: Effect of Spinal Cord Transaction on the Base Composition and Content of RNA in the Mauthner Nerve Fiber of the Goldfish. *J. Neurochem., 11:*557-559, 1964.
110. Efron, R.: The Conditioned Reflex. A Meaningless Concept. *Persp. in Biol. and Med., 9:*488-514, 1966; *Intern. J. Psychiat., 4:*938-417, 1967.
111. Egyhazi, E. and Hydén, H.: Experimentally Induced Changes in the Base Composition of the Ribonucleic Acids of Isolated Nerve Cells and their Oligodendroglial Cells. *J. Biophys. Biochem. Cytol., 10:*403-410, 1961.
112. Eichenwald, H. F. and Fry, P. C.: Nutrition and Learning. *Science, 163:*644-648, 1969.
113. Eigen, M.: *Neurosc. Res. Progr. Bull., 2:*11-22, 1964; quoted by Schmitt, F. O. (Ref. 358a).
114. Elkind, D.: Giant in the Nursery—Jean Piaget. *The New York Times Magazine,* May 26, 1968, 11-25-80.
115. Elmgrem, J.: *Some Fundamental Problems in Psychological Factor Analysis.* Göteborg, University of Göteborg Press, 1958.

116. El-Sum, H.: Proceedings, Fifth Conference on Information and Control Processes in Living Systems. Pacific Palisades, California, February 23-26, 1969.

117. Essman, W. B.: Facilitation of Maze Acquisition by Mice with Tricyanoaminopropene (TCAP) Given During Early Postnatal Development. *Psychonom. Sci., 9:*51, 52, 1967.

118. Evans, C. H. and Mulholland, T. B.: Attention as a Concept in Neurophysiology. *Science, 163:*495, 496, 1969.

119. Ey, H.: Les Troubles de la Mémoire. *Études Psychiatriques, 9:* Paris, 1950.

120. Eysenck, H. J.: *The Dynamics of Anxiety and Hysteria.* New York, Praeger, 1957.

121. Fearing, F.: *Reflex Action.* New York, Hafner, 1964.

122. Feindel, W.: The Brain Considered as a Thinking Machine. In Feindel, W. (Ed.): *Memory, Learning, Language.* Toronto, University of Toronto Press, 1960.

123. Ferenczi, S., *The Problems and Methods in Psychoanalysis.* New York, Basic Books, 1955.

124. Fessard, A.: The Role of Neuronal Networks in Sensory Communication. In Rosenblith, W. A. (Ed.): *Sensory Communication.* New York, Wiley, 1961.

125. Fisher, C. M. and Adams, R. D.: Transient Global Amnesia. *Acta Psychiat. Neurol. Scand., Suppl. 9:*1964.

126. Fjerdingstad, E. J.: a) quoted by Halstead and Rucker. (Ref. 172); b) Proceedings, 135th Meeting, American Association Advancement Science, Dallas, 1968.

127. Flexner, J. B. and Flexner, L. B.: a) Restoration of Expression of Memory Lost after Treatment with Puromycin. *Proc. Nat. Acad. Sci. U. S. A., 57:*1651-1654, 1967; b) Puromycin Effect on Memory of the Mice when Injected with Various Cations. *Science, 165:*1143, 1144, 1969.

128. Flexner, J. B., Flexner, L. B., and Stellar, E.: a) Memory in Mice as Affected by Intracranial Puromycin. *Science, 141:*57-59, 1963; b) Memory Cerebral Protein Synthesis in Mice Affected by Gradual Amounts of Puromycin. *Exper. Neurol., 13:*264-272, 1965; c) Effects of Acetoxycycloheximide-Puromycin Mixture on Cerebral Protein Synthesis and Memory in Mice. *Proc. Nat. Acad. Sci., U. S. A., 55:*369-374, 1966.

129. Flexner, L. B., Flexner, J. B., and Roberts, R. B.: Memory in Mice Analyzed with Antibiotics. *Science, 55:*1377-1383, 1967.

130. Forgays, D. C. and Forgays, J. W.: The Nature of the Effect of Free-Environmental Experience in the Rat. *J. Comp. Physiol., 45:*322-328, 1952.

131. Frankenhauser, M., Myrsten, A. E., and Jarps, C.: Effects of a Moderate Dose of Alcohol on Intellectual Functions. *Psychopharmacology, 3:*344-351, 1962.

132. Fredericson, E., Fink, C. D., and Parker, J. R.: Elicitation and Inhibition of Competitive Fighting in Food-Deprived Mice. *J. Gen. Psychol.,* 86:131-144, 1955.
133. French, J. D.: The Reticular Formation. *Sci. Amer., 196:*54-60, 1957.
134. Freud, S.: a) *The Interpretation of Dreams.* London, Hogart Press, 1900; b) *Psychopathology of Everyday Life.* London, Hogart Press, 1901; c) *The Complete Work of Sigmund Freud.* London, Hogart Press, 1953.
135. Freyhan, F. A., Catalano, F., and Mayo, J. A.: Summary Report of Clinical Investigation of the Effects of Magnesium Pemoline (Abbott Cylert) on Memory Impairment of Geriatric Patients. *Compr. Psychiatr.,* in press.
136. Gaito, J.: a) DNA and RNA as Memory Molecules. *Psychol. Rev., 70:* 471-480, 1963; b) (Ed.), *Macromolecules and Behavior.* New York, Appleton-Century-Crofts, 1966.
137. Galambos, R.: a) Suppression of Auditory Nerve Activity by Stimulation of Efferent Fibers to Cochlea. *J. Neurophysiol., 19:*424-437, 1956; b) Changing Concepts on the Learning Mechanisms. In Delafresnaye, J. P. (Ed.). (Ref. 84); c) Proceedings 135th Meeting, American Association Advancement Science, Dallas, 1968.
138. Galavas, R.: Quoted in Probing the Brain's Deep Secrets. *Med. World News,* August 16, 28-35, 1968.
139. Garcia, J. and Ervin, F. R.: Appetites, Aversion and Addictions: A Model for Visceral Memory. *Rec. Adv. Biol. Psychiat., 10:*1967.
140. Gazzaniga, M. S.: Psychological Properties of the Disconnected Hemispheres in Man. *Science, 150:*372, 1965.
141. Gazzaniga, M. S. and Sperry, R. W.: Language After Sectioning of the Cerebral Commissures. *Brain, 90:*131-148, 1967.
142. Gazzaniga, M. S., Bogen, J. E., and Sperry, R. W.: a) Observation on Visual Perception After Disconnection of the Cerebral Hemispheres in Man. *Brain, 88:*221-236, 1964; b) Dispraxia Following Division of the Cerebral Commissures. *Arch. Neurol. Psychiatr., 16:*606-612, 1967.
143. Gelber, B.: Quoted by Halsteadt and Rucker. (Ref. 172).
144. Gerard, R. W.: a) What is Memory? *Sci. Amer., 189:*118-126, 1953; b) The Fixation of Experience. In Delafresnaye, J. P. (Ed.). (Ref. 90); c) Theoretical-Experiential Approaches to Memory. *J. Verb. Learn. Behav., 2:*22-23, 1963; d) Can Computer Help Build Better Brains? *Front. Hosp. Psychiatr., 5:*5, 8, 1968.
145. Gerbrandt, L.: Quoted by Pribram. (Ref. 330e).
146. Geschwind, N.: Disconnection Syndromes on Animals and Man. *Brain,* 88:237-294, 1965.
146a. Gilbert, R. M. and Sutherland, N. S. (Eds.): *Animal Discrimination Learning.* New York, Academic Press, 1969.

147. Giuditta, A.: Biosintesi e Funzione dell'RNA Cerebrale. *Acta Neurol.,* 23:511-528, 1968.
148. Glaser, R.: In Wittrock, M. C. and Wiley, D. (Eds.): *Evolution of Instruction.* New York, Holt, Rinehart and Winston, 1969.
149. Glasky, A. J. and Simon, L. M.: Magnesium Pemoline: Enhancement of Brain RNA Polymerase. *Science, 151:*702, 703, 1966.
150. Glassman, E.: The Biochemistry of Learning and Elaboration of the Role of RNA and Proteins. *Ann. Rev. Biochem., 38:*605-646, 1969.
151. Glees, P.: *Experimental Neurology.* Oxford, Clarendon Press, 1961.
152. Gleitman, H.: Place Learning Without Prior Performance. *J. Comp. Physiol. Psychol., 48:*77-79, 1955.
153. Glikman, S. E.: Perserveration of Neural Processes and the Consolidation of the Memory Trace. *Psychol. Bull., 58:*218-233, 1961.
154. Goddard, G. V.: Function of the Amygdala. *Psychol. Bull., 62:*89-110, 1964.
155. Goldstein, K. and Scheerer, M.: Abstract and Concrete Behavior: An Experimental Study in Special Tests. *Psychol. Monogr., 53:* No. 2, 1941.
156. Gorsky, R. A. and Whalen, R.: in Brazier, M. (Ed.): *Brain and Behavior.* Berkeley, University of California Press, 1966.
157. Granit, R.: a) *Sensory Mechanisms of Retina.* London, Oxford University Press, 1947; b) *Receptors and Sensory Perception.* Sillman Lectures. New Haven, Yale University Press, 1955.
158. Grant, D. A., Jones, O. R., and Tallantis, B.: The Relative Difficulty of the Number, Form and Color Concepts of a Weigl-type Problem. *J. Exp. Psychol., 39:*552-557, 1949.
159. Grenell, R. and Romero, E.: The Chemistry of Thought. *Med. World News, 11:*41-49, 1970.
160. Griffith, J. S.: *A View of the Brain.* London, Oxford University Press, 1967.
161. Griffith, J. S.: *Nature, 221:*520, 1969; quoted by Grenell and Romero. (Ref. 159).
162. Griffith, J. S. and Mahler, H. R.: DNA-Ticketing Theory of Memory. *Nature, 223:*580-582, 1969.
163. Grinker, R. R. and Spiegel, J. P.: *War Neuroses in North Africa.* Josiak Macy, Jr., Foundation, New York, 1943.
164. Grippo, P., Iaccarino, M., Parisi, E., and Scarano, E.: Methylation of DNA in Developing Urchin Embryos. *J. Mol. Biol., 36:*195-208, 1968.
165. Gross, R. F. and Birney, R. C. (Eds.): *Transfer of Learning: An Enduring Problem in Psychology.* New York, Van Nostrand, 1963.
166. Guilford, J. P.: a) *The Nature of Human Intelligence.* New York, McGraw-Hill, 1967; b) Intelligence Has Three Facets. *Science, 160:*615-620, 1970.

167. Gurowitz, E. M.: a) Effects of TCAP on Passive Avoidance Learning in the Rat. *Psychonom. Sci.*, *12*:293, 294, 1968; b) Some Effects of Injections of Brain Homogenates on Behavior. *Psychol. Rep.*, *23*:899-910, 1968.
168. Hall, C. S.: In Stevens, S. S. (Ed.): *Handbook of Experimental Psychology*. New York, Wiley, 1951.
169. Hall, E. A.: A conversation with Jean Piaget and Barbel Inhelder. *Psychol. Today*, *3*:25-32 and 54-56, 1970.
170. Halstead, W. C.: Biological Intelligence. *J. Personol.*, *20*:118-120, 1951.
171. Halstead, W. C. and Katz, J. J.: Protein Organization and Mental Function. *Comp. Psychol. Monogr.*, *20*:1-38, 1950.
172. Halstead, W. C. and Rucker, W. B.: Memory: A Molecular Maze. *Psychol. Today*, *2*:38-41 and 66, 67, 1968.
173. Harlow, H. F.: The Nature of Learning Sets. *Psychol. Rev.* 56:51-65, 1949.
174. Harlow, H. F. and Harlow, M. K.: Learning to Think. *Sci. Amer.*, *181*: 36-59, 1949.
175. Harris, J. D.: Habituatory Response Decrement in the Intact Organism. *Psychol. Bull.*, *40*:385-422, 1943.
176. Hartline, H. K.: Visual Receptors and Retinal Information. *Science*, *164*:270-278, 1969.
177. Hartry, A. L., Kleit-Lee, P., and Morton, W. W. D.: Planaria Memory Transfer through Cannibalism Re-examined. *Science*, *146*:274, 275, 1964.
178. Hebb, D. O.: *The Organization of Behavior*. *Neuropsychological Theory*. New York, Wiley, 1949.
179. Hediger, H.: *Studies of the Psychology and Behavior of the Captive Animals in Zoos and Circuses*. London, Butterworths, 1965.
180. Heidbreder, E.: The Attainment of Concepts. VI. Exploratory Experiments on Conceptualization at Perceptual Levels. *J. Psychol.*, *26*:193-216, 1948.
181. Helson, H. and Helson, H. B.: Some Common Features of Concrete and Abstract Thinking. *Amer. J. Psychol.*, *59*:458-472, 1946.
182. Hernandez-Péon, R., Scheerer, H., and Jouvet, M.: Modification of Electrical Activity in Cochlear Nucleus During Attention in Unanesthetized Cats. *Science*, *123*:331, 332, 1956.
183. Hess, E. L. Origins of Molecular Biology. *Science*, *168*:664-669, 1970.
184. Hess, W. R.: a) *Il Diencefalo*. Milano, Martello, 1949; b) *The Biology of Mind*. Chicago, University of Chicago Press, 1964.
185. Hicks, L. H.: An Analysis of Number-Concept Formation in the Rhesus Monkey. *J. Comp. Physiol. Psychol.*, *49*:212-218, 1956.
186. Hilgard, E. R.: *Theories of Learning*. New York, Appleton-Century-Crofts, 1956.

187. Hinton, R. T., Jr.: A Further Study of the Role of the Basal Metabolic Rate on the Intelligence of Children. *J. Edu. Psychol.*, *30*:309-314, 1939.
188. Hirsch, J.: In: Bliss, E. L. (Ed.): *Roots of Behavior*. New York, Harper, 1962.
189. Honig, W. K. (Ed.): *Operant Behavior: Areas of Research and Application*. New York, Appleton-Century-Crofts, 1966.
190. Horridge, G. A.: *Interneurons. Their Origin, Action, Specificity, Growth and Plasticity*. San Francisco, Freeman, 1968.
191. Hubel, D. H.: The Visual Cortex of the Brain. *Sci. Amer.*, *209*:754-762, 1963.
192. Hubel, D. H. and Wiesel, T. N.: Receptive Fields in the Striate Cortex of Very Young Usually Inexperienced Kittens. *J. Neurophysiol.*, *26*:944-1002, 1963.
193. Hughes, K. R., Cooper, R. M., and Zubek, J. P.: Effect of Glutamic Acid on the Learning Ability of Bright and Dull Rats. *Canad. J. Psychol.*, *11*:182-184 and 253-255, 1957.
194. Hulicka, J. M. and Grossman, J. L.: Age-Group Comparison for Mouse of Mediators in Paired-Associate Learning. *J. Gerontol.*, *22*:45-51, 1967.
195. Hull, C. L.: *Principles of Behavior*. New York, Appleton-Century-Crofts, 1943.
196. Humphrey, G. and Coxon, R. V.: *The Chemistry of Thinking*. Springfield, Thomas, 1963.
197. Humpries, B. M. and Jacobson, R.: *Worm Runner's Digest*, *3*:165-196, 1961; quoted by McConnell. (Ref. 270a).
198. Hunsperger, R. W.: La Répresentation Centrale des Résections Affectives dans le Cerveau Antérieur et dans le Tronc Cérébral. *Neurochirurgie*, *5*:207, 1959.
199. Hunter, I. M. L.: *Memory*. Baltimore, Penguin Books, 1964.
200. Hunter, W. S. and Sigler, M.: The Span of Visual Discrimination as a Function of Time and Intensity of Stimulation. *J. Exp. Psychol.*, *26*:160-179, 1940.
201. Hydén, H.: a) *Biochemistry of the Central Nervous System*. London, Pergamon, 1959; b) The Neuron and its Glia. A Biochemical and Functional Unit. *Endeavour*, *21*:144-155, 1962; c) *The Neuron*. New York, Elsevier, 1967; d) Experiments on Learning and Memory. *Psychiat. Spect.*, *5*:4, 5, 1968.
202. Hydén, H. and Egyhazi, E.: a) Nuclear Ribonucleic Acid (RNA) Changes of Nerve Cells During a Learning Experiment in Rats. *Proc. Nat. Acad. Sci. U. S. A.*, *48*:1366-1373, 1962; b) Glial Ribonucleic Acid (RNA) Changes during a Learning Experiment in Rats. *Proc. Nat. Acad. Sci. U. S. A.*, *49*:618-624, 1963; c) Changes in RNA Content and Basic Composition in Cortical Neurons of Rats in a Learning Experiment Involving Transfer of Handedness. *Proc. Nat. Acad. Sci. U. S. A.*, *52*:1030-1035, 1964.

203. Hydén, H. and Lange, P. W.: a) Differentiation in RNA Response in Neuron Early and Late During Learning. *Proc. Nat. Acad. Sci. U. S. A.*, 53:946-952, 1965; b) Protein Synthesis in the Hippocampal Pyramidal Cells of the Rats During a Behavioral Test. *Science, 159*:200, 201, 1969.
204. Ingbar, S. H.: The Action of 1,1,3-tricyano-2-amino-1-propene (U-9189) on the Thyroid Gland of the Rat and Its Effects in Human Thyrotoxicosis. *J. Clin. Endocrinol., 21*:128-139, 1961.
205. Isaacson, R. I. (Ed.): *The Neuropsychology of Development*. A Symposium. New York, Wiley, 1968.
206. Jacob, J. and Sirlin, J. L.: Synthesis of RNA *in vitro* stimulated in Dipteran Salivary Glands by 1,1,3-tricyano-2-amino-1-propene. *Science, 144*: 1011, 1012, 1964.
207. Jacobson, A. L.: Learning in Flatworms and Annelids. *Psychol. Bull., 60*:74-94, 1963.
208. Jaffe, D. S.: Forgetting and Remembering: Defensive Cathectic Shift as a Determinant of Parapraxis and its Resolution. *Psychiat. Spect., 5*: 7, 8, 1969.
209. Janet, P.: Preface to Delay, J., *Les Dissolutions de la Mémoire*. Paris, Presse Universitaire de France, 1942.
210. Jarvik, M. E.: a) In Steinberg, H. (Ed.). (Ref. 384); b) In Bovet, D. *et al.* (Eds.): *Recent Advances in Learning and Retention*, Suppl. 109, Roma, Acc. Naz. Lincei, 1968.
211. Jasper, J. J.: Implications for the Neurological Studies. In Sheer, D. E. (Ed.): *Electrical Stimulation of the Brain*. Austin, University of Texas Press, 1961.
212. John, E. R.: The Front-Stoop Approach to Memory. *Persp. Biol. Med., 9*:35-53, 1965.
213. John, E. R.: *Mechanisms of Memory*. New York, Academic Press, 1967.
214. John, E. R., Chesler, P., Victor, R., and Bartlett, F.: Observation Learning in Cats. *Science, 159*:1489-1491, 1968.
215. Joseph, E. D.: Memory and Conflict. *Psychoanal. Quart., 35*:1-17, 1966.
216. Jouvet, M., Schott, R., Courjon, J., and Allegra, G.: Documentes Neurophysiologiques Relatifs au Mechanismes de l'Attention Chez l'Homme. *Rev. Neurol., 100*:437-450, 1959.
217. Jung, C. O.: *The Archetypes and the Collective Unconscious*, Collected Works, Vol. 9. New York, Pantheon, 1953.
218. Kamin, L.: quoted by Halstead and Rucker. (Ref. 172).
219. Kantor, J. R.: *The Scientific Evaluation of Psychology*. Granville, Ohio, Principia, 1969.
220. Kaolousek, F. and Morris, W. R.: *J. Biol. Chem., 243*:2440, 1968; quoted by Griffith and Mahler. (Ref. 162).
221. Karsh, E. B.: Fixation Produced by Conflict. *Science, 168*:873-875, 1970.

222. Katkin, E. S. and Murray, E. M.: Instrumental Conditioning of Anatomically Mediated Behavior: Theoretical and Methodological Issues. *Psychol. Bull.*, 70:52-68, 1968.

223. Katz, D.: *Gestalt Psychology.* Basel, Benno-Schwalbe, 1948.

224. Katz, D. and Katz, R. (Eds.): *Handbuch der Psychologie.* Basel, Benno-Schwalbe, 1960.

225. Keller, H.: *The History of My Life.* New York, Doubleday, 1903.

226. Kennard, B. A.: Reorganization of Motor Function in Cerebral Cortex of Monkeys Deprived of Motor and Pre-Motor Areas in Infancy. *J. Neurophysiol.*, 1:477-496, 1938.

227. Kimble, D. P.: *Holgard and Marquis' Conditioning and Learning.* New York, Appleton-Century-Crofts, 1961.

228. Kimble, D. P. (Ed.): *The Anatomy of Memory.* Palo Alto, Calif., Science and Behavior Books, 1963.

229. Kimble, D. P. and Pribram, K. H.: Hippocampectomy and Behavior Sequences. *Science, 139:*824-825, 1963.

230. King, J. A.: Parameters Relevant to Determining the Effects of Early Experience upon the Adult Behavior of Animals. *Psychol. Bull., 55:*46, 1958.

231. Klein, M.: Proceeding Fifth Conference on Information and Control Processes in Living Systems. Pacific Palisades, Calif., February 23-26, 1969.

232. Kock, S. (Ed.): *Psychology: A Study of a Science.* New York, McGraw-Hill, 1959.

233. Koehler, W.: On the Nature of Association. *Proc. Amer. Phil. Soc., 84:* 489-502, 1941.

234. Koestler, A.: *The Art of Creation.* New York, Macmillan, 1964.

235. Koffka, K.: *Principles of Gestalt Psychology.* New York, Harcourt-Brace, 1935.

236. Konorski, J.: a) The Physiological Approach to the Problem of Recent Memory. In Delafresnaye, H. P. (Ed.). (Ref. 90); b) *Integrative Activity of the Brain. An Interdisciplinary Approach.* Chicago, University of Chicago Press, 1967.

237. Kopp, R., Bohdanecky, Z., and Jarvik, B. E.: Long Temporal Gradient of Retrograde Amnesia for a Well Discriminated Stimulus. *Science, 153:* 1547-1549, 1966.

238. Kove, H., Grabow, J., and Tritez, R. L.: Quoted in: Barbiturate Spots Memory Deficit After Lobectomy. *Med. Trib., 12:*3, 1969.

239. Kraepelin, E.: Über Erinnerungs Falsckungen. *Arch. Psychiat., 17:* 830-843; *18:*199-239 and 395-436, 1887.

240. Krahl, V. A.: Senescent Forgetfulness: Benign and Malignant. *Cand. Med. Ass. J., 86:*257-260, 1962.

241. Krahl, V. A. and Durost, H. B.: A Comparative Study of the Amnesia Syndrome in Various Organic Conditions. *Amer. J. Psychiat., 110:*41-47, 1953.

242. Krech, D., Rosenzweig, M. R., and Bennet, E. L.: Effects of Environmental Complexity and Training in Brain Chemistry. *J. Comp. Physiol. Psychol., 53:*509-519, 1960.

243. Kuffler, S. W. and Nicholls, J. G.: The Physiology of Neuroglial Cells. *Ergebn. Physiol., 57:*1-90, 1966.

244. Kuhlembeck, H.: *Mind and Matter: An Appraisal of the Significance for Neurologic Theory.* Basel, Karger, 1961.

245. Kupfermann, I., Castellucci, V., Pinsker, V., and Kandel, E. R.: Neuronal Correlates of Habituation and Dishabituation in the Gill-Withdrawal Reflex in *Aplysia. Science, 167:*1743-1745, 1970.

246. La Grutta, G.: Problemi di Fisiologia della Barriera Emato-Encefalica. *Acta Neurol., 23:*1062-1075, 1968.

247. Landauer, J. K.: Two Hypotheses Concerning the Biochemical Basis of Memory. *Psychol. Rev. 71:*167-179, 1965.

248. Langs, R. J.: Stability of Earliest Memories Under LSD-25 and Placebo. *J. Nerv. Ment. Dis., 144:*171-184, 1967.

249. Lark, C.: Effects of Methionine Analogs, Ethionine and Norleucine on DNA Synthesis in *Escherichia Coli* 15 T. *J. Mol. Biol., 31:*401-404, 1968.

250. Lashley, K. S.: a) *Brain Mechanisms and Intelligence.* Chicago, University of Chicago Press, 1929; b) Integrative Functions of Cerebral Cortex. *Psychol. Rev., 13:*1-42, 1933; c) Functional Determinants of Cerebral Localization. *Arch. Neurol. Psychiat.* 38:371-387, 1937; d) Coalescence of Neurology and Psychology. *Proc. Amer. Phil. Soc., 84:* 461-470, 1941; e) In Search of the Engram. In Danielli, J. F. and Brown, R. (Eds.): *Physiological Mechanisms of Animal Behavior.* London, Cambridge University Press, 1950; f) The Problem of Serial Order in Behavior. In Jeffer, L. A. (Ed.): *Cerebral Mechanisms in Behavior.* The Hixon Symposium. New York, Wiley, 1951.

251. Lashley, W.: quoted by Luce, G. (Ref. 260).

252. Leith, E. M. and Upatnicks, J.: Photography by Laser. *Sci. Amer.:* June 1965; quoted by Pribram, K. H. (Ref. 330e).

253. Levine, S.: Infantile Experience and Resistance to Physiological Stress. *Science, 126:*405, 1957.

254. Lewy, E. and Rappaport, D.: The Psychoanalytic Concept of Memory and its Relation to Recent Memory Traces. *Psychoanal. Quart., 13:*16-42, 1944.

255. Liddell, E. G. T.: *The Discovery of Reflexes.* London, Oxford University Press, 1960.

256. Lindsley, D. B.: Address to the Western Psychological Association. Vancouver, Canada, June 1969.

257. Livingston, R. B.: Proceedings, 135th Meeting, American Association Advancement Science, Dallas, 1968.

258. Lorente de No', R.: Analysis of the Activity of the Chain of the Internuncial Neurons. *J. Neurophysiol., 1*:207-244, 1938.

259. Lorenz, K.: *Studies in Animal and Human Behavior.* Cambridge, Harvard University Press, 1970.

260. Luce, G.: Biological Bases of Memory. *Mental Health Program Reports, 4:* Publ. No. 5026, 1970.

261. Luria, A. R.: a) *Human Brain and Psychological Processes.* New York, Harper, 1966; b) *The Mind of a Mnemonist. A Little Book About a Vast Memory.* New York, Basic Books, 1968.

262. Luttges, M., Johnson, T., Ruck, C., Jolland, J., and McGaugh, J.: An Examination of the Transfer of Learning by Nucleic Acid. *Science, 151:* 834-837, 1966.

263. Macchi, G.: Aspetti della Organizzazione Anatomo-Funzionale delle Strutture Rinencefaliche. *Acta Neurol., 23:*965-1021, 1968.

264. MacKay, D. M.: Neural Communications: Experiments and Theory. *Science, 159:*335-353, 1968.

265. MacLean, P. D.: Studies on Limbic System (Visceral Brain) and Their Bearing on Psychosomatic Problems. In Wittkower, E. D. and Cleghorn, R. A. (Eds.): *Recent Developments in Psychosomatic Medicine.* London, Sir Isaac Pitman and Sons, Ltd., 1954.

266. Madsen, M.: quoted by Luce, G. (Ref. 260).

267. Magoun, H. W.: *The Waking Brain.* Springfield, Thomas, 1958.

267a. Mascherpa, P.: I Mnemofarmaci. *Rass. Clin. Sci., 46:*129-139, 1970.

268. Masserman, J. H. and Rubinfine, D. L.: "Counting" Behavior in Cats. *J. Gen. Psychol., 30:*87, 88, 1944.

269. Mayor, S. J.: Memory in the Japanese Quail; Effects of Puromycin and Acetoxycycloheximide. *Science, 166:*1165-1167, 1969.

270. McConnell, J. V.: a) Memory Transfer through Cannibalism in Planarians. *J. Neurophysiol., 3:*42-48, 1962; b) On the Turning of the Worms: A Reply to James and Males. *Psychol. Res., 14:*13-20, 1964; c) Cannibals, Chemicals and Contiguity. *Animal Behav., Suppl.:* 61-66, 1965.

271. McConnell, J. V., Jacobson, A. L., and Kimble, D. F.: The Effects of Regeneration Upon Retention of a Conditioned Response in the Planarian. *J. Comp. Physiol. Psychol., 52:*1-5, 1959.

272. McConnell, J. V., Jacobson, R., and Humphries, B. M.: *Worm Runner's Digest, 3:*41-47, 1961; quoted by McConnell, J. V. (Ref. 270a).

273. McGaugh, J. L.: a) Time Dependent Processes in Memory Storage. *Science, 153:*1351-1358, 1966; b) quoted by Hoagland, H., in Schmitt, F. O. (Ref. 358); c) quoted by Luce, G., see quot. 260.

274. McGaugh, J. L. and Petrinovich, L. F.: Effects of Drugs on Learning and Memory. *Intern. Rev. Neurobiol., 8:*139-196, 1965.

275. McGaugh, J. L., Weinberg, N. M., and Whalen, R. E. (Eds.): *Psychobiology. The Biological Basis of Behavior.* San Francisco, Freeman, 1967.

276. McGeoch, J. A.: *Psychology of Human Learning.* London, Longmans, 1951.

277. Meier, H.: in *Experimental Pharmacogenetics.* New York, Academic Press, 1963.

278. Weissner, W. W.: Hippocampal Functions in Learning. *J. Psychol. Res., 41:*235-304, 1966.

279. Mekler, L. B.: Mechanisms of Biologic Memory. *Nature, 215:*481-484, 1967.

279a. Melges, F. T., Tinklemberg, J. R., Hollister, L. E., and Gillespie, H. K.: Marihuana and Temporal Disintegration. *Science, 168:*1118-1120, 1970.

280. Melton, A. W.: a) Implications of Short-Term Memory for a General Theory of Memory. *J. Verb. Learn. Verb. Behav., 2:*1-21, 1963; b) (Ed.): *Categories of Human Learning.* New York, Academic Press, 1964.

281. Merleau-Ponty, M.: *The Structure of Behavior.* Boston, Beacon Press, 1963.

282. Meselson, M. and Yuan, R.: DNA Restriction Enzyme from *E. Coli. Nature, 217:*1010-1014, 1968.

283. Miller, G. A.: *Psychology: The Science of Mental Life.* New York, Harper, 1962.

284. Miller, G. A., Galanter, E., and Pribram, K. H.: *Plans and the Structure of Behavior.* New York, Holt, Rinehart and Winston, 1960.

285. Miller, N. E.: Learning of Visceral and Glandular Responses. *Science, 163:*433-445, 1969.

286. Miller, N. E. and Dollard, J.: *Social Learning and Imitation.* New Haven, Yale University Press, 1941.

287. Milner, B.: a) Memory Disturbance After Bilateral Hippocampal Lesions. In Milner, P. M. and Glickman, S. E. (Eds.): *Cognitive Processes and the Brain.* New York, Van Nostrand, 1965; b) quoted by Luce, G. (Ref. 260).

288. Misanin, J. R., Miller, R. R., and Lewis, J. D.: Retrograde Amnesia Produced by Electroconvulsive Shock After Reactivation of a Consolidated Memory Trace. *Science, 160:*554, 555, 1968.

289. Mokrasch, L. C. and Manner, P.: Incorporation of 14-Aminoacids and 14-Palmitate intro Proteolipids of Rat Brains *in vitro. J. Neurochem., 10:* 541-547, 1963.

290. Mosler, U.: *The Worm Runner's Digest,* 8:48-63, 1966; quoted by Guilford. (Ref. 166).

291. Mowrer, O. H.: a) *Learning, Theory and Personality Dynamics.* New York, Ronald Press, 1950; b) *Learning, Theory and Behavior.* New York, Wiley, 1960.

292. Müller, G. E. and Pilzecher, A.: Experimentelle Beitrage sur Lehre von Gedachtniss. *Z. Psychol. Bull., Ergebn. 1:*1900.
293. Mumenthaler, M. and von Bell, L.: Transient Global Amnesia. *Schweitz. Med. Wschr., 99:*113-139, 1969.
293a. Nachmanson, D.: a) *Chemical and Molecular Basis of Nerve Activity.* New York, Academic Press, 1959; b) Proteins in Excitable Membranes. *Science, 168:*1059-1066, 1970.
294. Nash, H.: *Alcohol and Caffeine: A Study of Their Psychological Effects.* Springfield, Thomas, 1962.
295. Nauta, W. J. H.: Some Brain Structures and Functions Related to Memory. *Neurosci. Res. Progr. Bull., 2:*1-35, 1964.
296. Neuman, van J.: *The Computer and the Brain.* New Haven, Yale University Press, 1958.
297. Newell, A., Shaw, J. C., and Simon, H. A.: Elements of a Theory of Problem Solving. *Psychol. Rev., 65:*151-166, 1958.
298. Nurnberger, J. I., Ferster, C. B., and Brady, J. P.: *An Introduction to the Science of Human Behavior.* New York, Appleton-Century-Crofts, 1963.
299. Obrador, S., Dierssen, G., and Pelaz, E.: Psicocirurgia en el Nivel Diencefalo-Hipothalamico. *Archivos de Neurobiol., 30:*275, 1967.
300. Odens, M.: Quoted in: RNA Taken from Cattle Held to Improve Memory in Elderly. *Med. Trib., 10:*2, 1969.
301. Oettinger, A. G.: *Run, Computer, Run.* Cambridge, Harvard University Press, 1969.
301a. Ojemann, G. and Fedio, P.: Effect of Stimulation of Human Thalamus and Parietal and Temporal White Matter on Short-Term Memory. *J. Neurosurg., 29:*51-59, 1968.
302. Olds, J.: Pleasure Centers in the Brain. *Sci. Amer., 195:*105-116, 1956.
303. Olds, J. and Milner, P.: Positive Reinforcement Produced by Electrical Stimulation of Septal Area and Other Regions of Rat Brain. *J. Comp. Physiol. Psychol., 47:*419-427, 1954.
304. Osborn, A. F.: *Applied Imagination.* New York, Scribner, 1963.
305. Osborn, A. G., Bunker, J. F., Cooper, L. M., Frank, G. S., and Hilgard, E. R.: Effects of Thiopenthal Sedation in Learning and Memory. *Science, 157:*574-576, 1967.
306. Oshima, K., Gorbman, A., and Shimada, H.: Memory-blocking Agents. Effects on Olfactory Discrimination in Homing Salmon. *Science, 165:*86-88, 1969.
307. Otis, L. S. and Prior, G. T.: Lack of Effect of TCAP on Conditioned Avoidance Learning on Rats. *Psychonom. Sci., 11:*95, 96, 1968.
308. Pacifico, C.: *Creative Thinking in Practice.* Park Ridge, N. J., Noyes, 1966.
309. Papez, J. W.: A Proposed Mechanism of Emotion. *Arch. Neurol. Psychiat., 38:*725-743, 1937.

310. Papo, I. and Caruselli, G.: Coagulazione Rostrale del Cingolo nei Dolori e nell'Aggressivita'. *Acta Neurol., 24*:94-101, 1969.

311. Paul, I. H.: Studies in Remembering. *Psychol. Issues, I:* No. 2, 1959.

312. Pavlov von, I. P.: *Lectures on Conditioned Reflexes.* London, Oxford University Press, 1927.

313. Pearlman, C. A., Jr., Sharpless, S. K., and Jarvik, M. E.: Retrograde Amnesia Produced by Anaesthetics and Convulsant Agents. *J. Comp. Physiol. Psychol., 54*:109-112, 1961.

314. Penfield, W.: a) Studies of the Cerebral Cortex of Man. A Review and an Interpretation. In: Adrian, E. D., Bremer, F., and Jasper, H. H. (Eds.): *Brain Mechanisms and Consciousness.* London, Blackwell, 1954; b) The Permanent Record of the Stream of Consciousness. *Acta Psychol., 11*:47-69, 1955; c) Some Mechanisms of Consciousness Discovered During the Electrical Stimulation of the Brain. *Proc. Acad. Sci., 44*:51-66, 1958; d) The Role of Temporal Cortex in Recall of Past Experience and Interpretation of the Present. Ciba Foundation Symposium on Neural Basis of Behavior. London, 1958.

315. Penfield, W. and Jaspers, H.: *Epilepsy and the Functional Anatomy of the Human Brain.* Boston, Little, Brown, 1954.

316. Penfield, W. and Milner, B.: The Memory Deficit Produced by Bilateral Lesions in the Hippocampal Zone. *Arch. Neurol. Psychiat., 79*:475-497, 1958.

317. Penfield, W. and Roberts, L.: *Speech and Brain Mechanisms.* Princeton, Princeton University Press, 1959.

318. Petersch, L. R.: Short-Term Verbal Memory and Learning. *Psychol. Rev., 73*:193-207, 1966.

319. Peterson, L. R. and Peterson, M. J.: Short-Term Retention of Individual Verbal Items. *J. Exper. Psychol., 58*:193-198, 1959.

320. Petrinovich, L. and Bliss, D.: Retention of a Learned Brightness Discrimination Following Ablation of the Occipital Cortex in the Rat. *J. Comp. Physiol. Psychol., 61*:136-138, 1966.

321. Pfeiffer, J. E.: *The Emergence of Man.* New York, Harper and Row, 1969.

322. Phillips, A. G., Cox, V. C., Kakolowski, J. W., and Valenstein, E. S.: Object Carrying by Rats: An Approach to the Behavior Produced by Brain Stimulation. *Science, 166*:903-905, 1969.

323. Piaget, J.: *Origins of the Intelligence.* New York, International University Press, 1964.

324. Pinsker, H., Kupfermann, I., Castellucci, V., and Kandel, E. R.: Habituation and Dishabituation of the Gill-Withdrawal Reflex in *Aplysia. Science, 167*:1740-1742, 1970.

325. Plotnikoff, N.: Magnesium Pemoline: Enhancement of Learning and Memory of a Conditioned Response. *Science, 151*:703, 704, 1966.

326. Porteus, S. D.: *The Maze Test and Clinical Psychology.* Palo Alto, Calif., Pacific Books, 1959.

327. Posner, M. I.: Immediate Memory in Sequential Tasks. *Psychol. Bull.,* 60:333-349, 1963.

328. Posner, M. I. and Rossman, E.: Effect of Size and Location of Informational Transforms Upon Short-Term Retention. *J. Exper. Psychol.,* 70: 496-505, 1965.

329. Postman, L.: Short-Term Memory and Incidental Learning. In Melton, A. W. (Ref. 280b).

330. Pribram, K. H.: a) A review of Theory on Physiological Psychology. *Ann. Rev. Psychol.,* 11:1-40, 1960; b) Implication for Systematic Study of Behavior. In Scheerer, D. E. (Ed.): *Electrical Stimulation of the Brain.* Austin, University of Texas Press, 1961; c) Some Dimensions of Remembering: Steps Toward a Neurophysiological Model of Memory. In Gaito, J. (Ed.): *Macromolecules and Behavior.* New York, Appleton-Century-Crofts, 1966; d) On Memory II. *Psychiat. Spect.,* 5:3, 4, 1968; e) The Neurophysiology of Remembering. *Sci. Amer.,* 220:73-86, 1969.

331. Pribram, K. H. and Bagshaw, M.: quoted by Pribram. (Ref. 330e).

331a. Pribram, K. H. and Broadbent, D. E.: *Biology of Memory.* New York, Academic Press, in press.

332. Pribram, K. H. and Fulton, J. P.: An Experimental Critique of the Effects of Anterior Cingulate Ablation in Monkey. *Brain,* 77:34, 1954.

333. Quartermain, D., Paolino, R. M., and Miller, N. E.: A Brief Temporal Gradient of Retrograde Amnesia Independent of Situational Change. *Science,* 149:1116-1118, 1965.

334. Quarton, G. C., Melnechuck, T., and Schmitt, F. O.: *The Neurosciences.* New York, The Rockefeller University Press, 1967.

335. Quasler, H.: *Information Theory in Psychology.* Chicago, The Free Press, 1965.

336. Rapaport, D.: a) *Emotions and Memory.* Baltimore, Williams and Wilkins, 1942; b) *Organization and Pathology of Thought.* New York, Columbia University Press, 1951.

337. Rappoport, D. A. and Daginawala, H. F.: *J. Neurochem.,* 15:991, 1968; quoted by Oshima *et al.* (Ref. 306).

337a. Reinis, S.: Block of "Memory Transfer" by Actinomycin D. *Nature,* 220:177, 178, 1968.

338. Ressler, R. H., *J. Comp. Physiol. Psychol.,* 56:882, 1963; quoted by Bovet, D. *et al.* (Ref. 44).

339. Retif, J., Crahay, S., and Brihaye, J.: Leucotomie Frontale à Minima Avec Interruption Sélective du Faiseau Cingulaire Uni- our Bilaterale dans le Traitment Chirurgical de la Douleur. *Acta Neurol. Belg.,* 66:499-513, 1966.

340. Rheingold, H. L. and Eckerman, C. O.: The Infant Separates Himself from his Mother. *Science,* 168:78-83, 1970.

341. Ribot, T. A.: *The Diseases of Memory*. New York, Appleton-Century-Crofts, 1882.
342. Rizzo, E. M.: Sulla Sindrome di Korsakoff. *Rass. Studi Psichiat., 44:* 800-816, 1955.
343. Robertson, H. D., Webster, R. E., and Zinder, N. D.: Purification and Properties of Ribonuclease III from *Escherichia Coli. J. Biol. Chem., 243:* 82-91, 1968.
344. Robinson, R.: *Genetics of the Norway Rat*. Oxford, Pergamon Press, 1965.
345. Robles, B., Ramos-Calvan, R., and Cravioto, J.: Evaluation of the Behavior of the Child with Advanced Malnutrition and of its Modifications during Recovery (Preliminary Report). *Bull. Med. Hosp. Inf. Mexico, 16:*317-341, 1959.
346. Rodieck, B. W.: quoted by Pribram, K. H. (Ref. 330e).
347. Rosemblatt, F. and Miller, R. G.: Behavioral Essay Procedures for Transfer of Learned Behavior in Brain Extracts. *Proc. Nat. Acad. Sci. U. S. A., 56:*1423-1430 and 1683-1688, 1966.
348. Rosenzweig, M. R.: Environmental Complexity, Cerebral Changes and Behavior. *Psychol., 21:*321-330, 1966.
349. Rosenzweig, M. R., Bennet, E. L., and Krech, D.: Supplementary Report. Cerebral Effects of Environmental Complexity and Training Among Adults Rats. *J. Comp. Physiol. Psychol., 57:*438, 439, 1964.
350. Rosvold, H. E. and Miskin, M.: Evolution of the Effects of Prefrontal Lobotomy on Intelligence. *Canad. J. Psychol., 4:*122-126, 1950.
351. Royce, J. R. and Covington, M.: Genetic Differences in the Avoidance Conditioning of Mice. *J. Comp. Physiol. Psychol., 53:*197-200, 1960.
352. Rucker, W. B. and Halstead, W. C.: Antagonistic Transfer Effects. In *Molecular Approaches to Learning and Memory*. Proc., 134th Meeting American Association Advancement Science, New York, 1967.
353. Russel, W. R.: *Brain, Memory, Learning*. Fair Lawn, N. J., Oxford, 1959.
354. Samuels, J.: Reticular Mechanisms and Behavior. *Psychol. Bull., 56:* 1-25, 1959.
355. Schaeffer, R. W.: Learning Without Running in a Y-Maze. *Psychol. Res., 14:*95-99, 1964.
356. Schlesinger, K. and Wimer, R.: Genotype and Conditioned Avoidance Learning in a Mouse. *J. Comp. Physiol. Psychol., 63:*139-141, 1967.
357. Schmidt, M. J. and Davenport, J. W.: TCAP: Facilitation of Learning in Hypothyroid Rats. *Psychonom. Sci., 7:*185, 186, 1967.
358. Schmitt, F. O.: a) (Ed.): *Horizons in Biochemistry*. New York, Academic Press, 1962; b) In Lyght, C. E. (Ed.): *Reflections on Research and the Future of Medicine*. New York, McGraw-Hill, 1967; c) Fifth Conference on Information and Control Processes in Living Systems. Pacific Palisades, Calif., February 23-25, 1969.

359. Scholes, N. W. and Wheaton, L. G.: Critical Period for Detour Learning in Developing Chicks. *Life Sci.*, 5:1859-1865, 1966.
360. Scrimshaw, N. S. and Gordon, J. E. (Eds.): *Malnutrition, Learning and Behavior.* Cambridge, M. I. T. Press, 1968.
361. Scuri, D.: *Il Linguaggio dell'Udente Normale e nel Sordomuto.* Roma, Pozzi, 1932.
361a. Sechzer, J. A.: Prolonged Learning in Split-Brain Cats. *Science, 169:* 889-892, 1970.
362. Shashoua: Quoted by Hydén. (Ref. 201d).
363. Sheid, B., Srinivasan, P. R., and Borek, E.: Deoxyribonucleic Acid Methylase of Mammalian Tissues. *Biochemistry*, 1:260-285, 1968.
364. Shepard, R. N.: Recognition Memory for Words, Sentences and Pictures. *J. Verb. Learn. Verb. Behav.*, 6:156-163, 1967.
365. Sherrington, C. S.: *The Integrative Action of the Nervous System.* New York, Scribner, 1906.
366. Shimazono, Y., Torii, H., Endo, M., Shara, S., Narukawa, H., and Matsuda, M.: Consequence of Thalamic and Sensory Afferent Impulses to Single Neurons in the Cortical Association Area of Cats. *Folia Psychiat. Neurol. Jap.*, 17:144-155, 1963.
367. Shure, G. H. and Halstead, W. C.: Cerebral Localization of Intellectual Processes. *Psychol. Monogr.*, 72: No. 12, 1958.
368. Shuttleworth, E. C. and Morris, C. E.: Transient Global Amnesia: Defect of Second Stage of Memory in Man. *Arch. Neurol.*, 15:515-520, 1966.
369. Skinner, B. P.: a) *The Behavior of Organisms.* New York, Appleton-Century-Crofts, 1938; b) *Science and Human Behavior.* New York, Macmillan, 1953.
370. Slukin, W.: *Imprinting and Early Learning.* Chicago, Aldine, 1965.
371. Smith, C. E.: Memory as a Matter of Enzyme Induction? *Science, 138:* 889, 890, 1962.
372. Snygg, D.: The Need for a Phenomenological System of Psychology. In Kuenzli, A. F. (Ed.): *The Phenomenological Problem.* New York, Harper, 1959.
373. Sokolow, R.: quoted by Pribram. (Ref. 330e).
374. Soutwick, C. H.: *Ecology, 36:627*, 1955; quoted by Bovet *et al.* (Ref. 44).
375. Spearman, C.: *The Abilities of Man.* London, Macmillan, 1927.
376. Sperry, R. W.: a) Psychological Plasticity and Brain Circuit Theory. In Harlow, H. F. and Woosley, C. N. (Eds.): *Biological and Biochemical Bases of Behavior.* Madison, University of Wisconsin Press, 1958; b) Cerebral Organization and Behavior. *Science, 133:*1749-1751, 1961; c) The Great Cerebral Commissure. *Sci. Amer., 210:*42-52, 1964.

377. Spong, P., Haider, W., and Lindley, D. B.: Selective Attentiveness and Cortical Evoked Responses to Visual and Auditory Stimuli. *Science, 148:*395-397, 1965.
378. Srinivasan, P. R. and Borek, E.: Enzymatic Alteration of Macromolecular Structures. *Progr. Nucl. Acid Res., 5:*157-189, 1966.
379. Staats, W. W.: a) (Ed.): *Human Learning.* New York, Holt, Rinehart and Winston, 1964; b) *Learning, Language and Cognition.* New York, Holt, Rinehart and Winston, 1969.
380. Stanley, W. C. and Jaynes, J.: The Function of the Frontal Cortex. *Psychol. Rev., 56:*18-32, 1949.
381. Stein, L.: In Efron, D. (Ed.): *Psychopharmacology. Review of Progress 1957-1967.* U. S. Gov. Printing Office, Washington, D. C., 1968.
382. Stein, D. C., Rosen, J. J., Graziadei, J., Miskin, D., and Brink, J. J.: Central Nervous System Recovery of Function. *Science, 166:*528-530, 1969.
383. Stein, L. and Berger, B. D.: Paradoxical Fear-Increasing Effects of Tranquilizers: Evidence of Repression of Memory in the Rat. *Science, 166:*253-256, 1969.
384. Steinberg, H. (Ed.): *Animal Behavior and Drug Addiction.* London, Churchill, 1964.
385. Stephens, G.: quoted by Luce, G. (Ref. 260).
386. Stevens, S. S.: *Handbook of Experimental Psychology.* New York, Wiley, 1951.
387. Stroebel, C.: quoted by Luce, G. (Ref. 260).
388. Stewart, L. W. and Ades, H. W.: The Factor in Reitegration of Learned Habit Lost after Temporal Lobe Lesions in Monkey *(Macaca Mulatta). J. Comp. Physiol. Psychol., 44:*479-486, 1951.
389. Suppes, F. and Morningstar, M.: Computer-Assisted Instruction. *Science, 166:*343-350, 1969.
390. Sussman, M. and Sussman, R.: In *Microbial Growth.* 19th Symposium of General Microbiology. London, Cambridge University Press, 1969.
391. Symonds, C.: Disorders of Memory. *Brain, 89:*625-644, 1966.
392. Talland, G. A.: a) *Deranged Memory: A Psychonomic Study of the Amnesic Syndrome.* New York, Academic Press, 1965; b) Amnesia: A World Without Continuity. *Psychol. Today, 1:*43-50, 1967; c) *Disorders of Memory and Learning.* New York, Penguin Books, 1968.
393. Talland, G. A., Hagen, D. Q., and James, M.: Performance Tests of Amnesic Patients with Cylert. *J. Nerv. Ment. Dis., 144:*421-429, 1967.
394. Teuber, H. L.: Neuropsychology. In Harris, R. E. (Ed.): *Recent Advances in Diagnostic Psychology.* Springfield, Thomas, 1960.
395. Thompson, R. F.: In Voss, J. F. (Ed.): *Approaches to Thought.* Columbus, Merril, 1969.

396. Thompson, R. and McConnell, J. V.: Classical Conditioning in the Planarian, *Dugesia Dorotouphala. J. Comp. Physiol. Psychol., 48*:65-68, 1955.

397. Thompson, R. F. and Shaw, J. A.: Behavorial Correlates of Evoked Activity Recorded from Association Areas of the Cerebral Cortex. *J. Comp. Physiol. Psychol., 60*:329-339, 1965.

398. Thompson, R. F. and Spencer, W. A.: Habituation: A Model Phenomenon for the Study of Neuronal Substrates of Behavior. *Psychol. Rev. 73*:16-43, 1966.

399. Thompson, R. F., Mayers, K. S., Robertson, R. T., and Patterson, C. J.: Number Coding in Association Cortex of the Cat. *Science, 168*:271-273, 1970.

400. Thompson, R. F., Bettinger, L. A., Birch, A., Groves, R. W., and Mayers, K. S.: *Neuropsychologia, 1*:217, 1969; quoted by Thompson, R. F. *et al.* (Ref. 399).

401. Thompson, W. R.: The Inheritance of Behavior. Behavioral Differences in Fifteen Mouse Strains. *Canad. J. Psychol., 7*:145-155, 1953.

402. Thorndike, E. I.: a) Animal Intelligence: An Experimental Study of the Associative Processes in Animals. *Psychol. Res. Monogr.*, Suppl. 2, No. 8, 1898; b) *Animal Intelligence.* New York, Macmillan, 1911.

403. Thorpe, W. H.: *Learning and Instinct in Animals.* Cambridge, Harvard University Press, 1958.

404. Tolman, E. C., Bitchis, B. F., and Kolish, D.: Studies in Spatial Learning. Part I. Orientation and the Short-Cut. Part II. Place-Learning versus Response-Learning. *J. Exper. Psychol., 36*:13-24 and 221-229, 1946.

404a. Torda, C.: Possible Relationship of Dreams on Engramming Long Term Memories. *Psychophysiol., 6*:253, 1969.

405. Triebwasser, S.: Large Scale Evolution and the Revolution in Electronics. *Science, 163*:429-435, 1969.

406. Troncale, L. R. and Ramsey-Klee, D. M.: Information and Control Processes in Living Systems. *Science, 166*:132-139, 1969.

407. Tryon, R. G.: In Moss, F. A. (Ed.): *Comparative Psychology.* Englewood Cliffs, N. J., Prentice-Hall, 1934.

408. Tulving, E.: Retrograde Amnesia in Free Recall. *Science, 164*:88-90, 1969.

409. Turner, V. W.: *The Ritual Process.* Chicago, Aldine, 1969.

410. Underwood, B. J.: Interference and Forgetting. *Psychol. Rev., 64*: 49-60, 1957.

411. Ungar, G.: a) Proceedings, 135th Meeting, American Association Advancement Science, Dallas, 1968; b) Molecular Mechanisms in Learning. *Persp. Biol. Med., 11*:217-232, 1968; c) The Chemistry of an Idea. *Med. Opin. Rev.*, 103-105, May 1969.

412. Valenzuela, R. H., Peniche, J. H., and Macias, R.: *Soc. Med. Hosp. Mexico, 89:*651, 1959; quoted by Eichenwald and Fry. (Ref. 112).

413. Vickery, B. C.: *On the Retrieval System Theory.* London, Butterworths, 1961.

414. Visintini, F.: Fisiopatologia della Memoria. *Acta Neurol., 3:*707, 1948.

415. Vizioli, R. and Bietti, C.: *Il Problema della Coscienza in Neuropsichiatria.* Pisa, Omnia Medica, 1966.

416. Wagman, A. M.: Effects of Frontal Lobe Lesions upon Behavior Requiring Use of Responded-Produced Cues. *J. Comp. Physiol. Psychol., 66:*69-76, 1968.

417. Watson, J. B.: a) *Behavior as Introduction to Comparative Psychology.* New York, Holt, Rinehart and Winston, 1914; b) Behaviourism: A Psychology Based on Reflexes. *Arch. Neurol. Psychiat., 15:*185-204, 1926.

418. Weiskrantz, L.: Neurological Studies. *Brit. Med. Bull., 20:*49-53, 1964.

419. Weissman, A.: Drugs and Retrograde Amnesia. *Intern. Rev. Neurobiol., 10:*167-198, 1967.

420. Wertheimer, M.: Untersuchungen zur Lehre von der Gestalt. *Psychol. Forech., 4:*167-198, 1967.

421. Whitty, C. W. M. and Zangwill, O. L. (Eds.): *Amnesia.* London, Butterworths, 1966.

422. Wikler, A.: *The Relation of Psychiatry to Pharmacology.* Baltimore, Williams and Wilkins, 1957.

423. Williams, M.: a) Memory Studies in ECT. *J. Neurol. Neurosurg. Psychiat., 13:*314-319, 1950; b) The Measurement of Memory in Clinical Practice. *Brit. J. Soc. Clin. Psychiat., 6:* in press.

424. Winick, M.: Fetal Malnutrition and Growth Processes. *Hosp. Pract., 5:*33-41, 1970.

425. Wise, R. A.: Hypothalamic Motivational Systems: Fixed or Plastic Neural Circuits. *Science, 162:*377, 378, 1968.

426. Woodworth, R. S. and Sheean, M. R.: *Contemporary Schools of Psychology.* New York, Holt, Rinehart and Winston, 1964.

427. Wooldridge, D. E.: *The Machinery of the Brain.* New York, McGraw-Hill, 1963.

428. Whorf, B. L.: *Language, Thought, Reality.* New York, Wiley, 1956.

429. Young, J. Z.: a) Some Essentials of Neural Memory Systems: Paired Center that Regulate and Addresses the Signal of the Results of Action. *Nature, 198:*620-632, 1964; b) *A Model of the Brain.* London, Oxford University Press, 1964; c) *The Memory System of the Brain.* Berkeley, University of California Press, 1966; d) Clinical Tests for Memory Impairment. *Proc. Roy. Soc. Med., 36:*576-580, 1943.

430. Zangwill, O. L.: Neurological Studies on Human Behavior. *Brit. Med. Bull., 20:*43-48, 1964.

431. Zemp, J. W., Wilson, J. E., and Glassman, E.: Brain Function and Macromolecules. II. Site of Increased Labeling of RNA in Brains of Mice During a Short-Term Training Experience. *Proc. Nat. Acad. Sci. U. S. A.,* 58:1120-1125, 1967.

432. Zemp, J. W., Wilson, J. E., Schlesinger, E., Boggan, W. O., and Glassman, E.: Brain Function and Macromolecules. I. Incorporation of Uridine into RNA of Mouse Brain During Short-Term Training Experience. *Proc. Nat. Acad. Sci. U. S. A.* 55:1423-1431, 1966.

433. Zubek, J. P. (Ed.): *Sensory Deprivation.* New York, Appleton-Century-Crofts, 1969.

INDEX